The Author's Accountability

Planner

A Day-by-Day Guide for Writers

"Because Writing is Hard."

2021

4 Horsemen
Publications, Inc.

4 Horsemen Publications, Inc.
1497 Main St. Suite 169
Dunedin, FL 34698
4horsemenpublications.com
info@4horsemenpublications.com

Typesetting by Battle Goddess Productions
Authored by Erika Lance, JM Paquette, Valerie Willis, and Vanessa Valiente

Paperback ISBN: 978-1-64450-129-0

DEDICATION

To all the great writers working on achieving
their dreams!

INTRODUCTION

"Guys, I need this in my life: An Author Accountability Guide."
The Researcher

"Yeah, we should do that!"　　　*The Architect*

"That's a great idea! Someone should do that!"
The Cheerleader

And so we became Someone.　　*The Taskmaster*

Once upon a time, there were four Muses who decided to create a planner/ guide for writers. This magical book would be a new resource for those seeking to set goals, track progress (not just word count), and enjoy the Muse-inspired motivation to stick with it for an entire year. Thus, the Author's Accountability Planner was born.

We hope authors find this book useful through each stage of their writing journey. Writing and creating, whether full-time or part-time, require time and organization. This planner is designed to help track time, provide recommendations, and share what the Muses have discovered to be game changers on their own journeys.

Throughout the year, everyone faces the challenges of self-doubt, procrastination, and Life in General (Remember the 2020 pandemic jolting everyone around the globe?). It's okay! Every week, the Muses are here to guide you through this adventure.

We will get through this together.

How to Use This Book

The Muses have spent countless hours fine-tuning the functionality of this book (by deciding if it should record writing time or beyond that). In the end, the Muses decided to account for all of the time spent doing writer-type things (brainstorming, writing, researching, editing, marketing, etc.). Many books discuss word count, but so much more happens before, after, and during the process of laying a book on paper (both physically and digitally).

Finishing the story is the single most important and difficult part of being a writer. To succeed, writers need accountability, someone or something to keep them motivated week after week. The Muses are here to keep the adventure moving forward, fight writer's block, and offer strategies to achieve year-end goals. Life is unpredictable, offering a variety of momentum-destroying reasons. This book can help you fight through those tough times while maintaining high morale.

In the end, only YOU can write YOUR story. You're here now, ready to do this. Let's go!

THE LAYOUT

This book contains four parts: Introductory Material (you're here!), Goal Setting, Month-by-Month Tracking, and Year Review. Each month has three sections: Monthly Prep, Weekly Overviews, and Monthly Review.

TRACKING DAILY ACCOMPLISHMENTS

Authors know that writing is more than sitting in a chair and putting words to paper (or screen). Word count is only one component of the writing process. A whole realm of prepping, marketing, research, and editing gets left out of all those other planners! We want you to be accountable by tracking all of the time you devote to your writing. Throughout this planner, the Muses have divided daily writing time into several different categories: Word Count, Brainstorming, Editing, Marketing, Research, and Reading.

Track your progress in these categories every day. It's okay to put a zero in a few places and focus on one task. Reviewing this information later can be

DAILY ACCOMPLISHMENTS	FRIDAY 29
WORD COUNT:_____	MARKETING HOURS:_____
BRAINSTORMING HOURS:_____	RESEARCH HOURS:_____
EDITING HOURS:_____	READING HOURS:_____

eye-opening when you compare good and bad weeks. In the end, use these pages to fine-tune your writing schedule, optimizing your output for all your writing needs. Some of us perform better when pairing tasks with one another; other times we reach higher word counts after reading and researching. Use these numbers to maximize your potential and make goal setting more rewarding.

WORD COUNT

You know this one! Word count is a common measure among authors to track their progress.

BRAINSTORMING

Some of us are pantsers while others are plotters. At times, we combine strategies! Either way, we spend some time prepping a story, even if it's an hour at the cafe writing on a napkin.

EDITING

Most writers work on more than one project at a time. Divide your attention between writing one work while editing another. One story might be completely drafted but still needs revision and editing. This step should never be skipped—whether posting to a blog or pitching to agents or publishers. Check your work.

MARKETING

If you dream to be famous, build awareness, or publish books, it's important to keep your author platform active by engaging on social media, writing blogs, posting advertisements, sending out newsletters, hosting events, and more. Automate as much as possible, scheduling your posts in advance to give yourself more time to create content. Don't risk losing your reader's interest!

RESEARCH

Whether researching how to buy a horse or a new method for writing dialogue, count your time. You're working! As a writer no less! These hours count too. ting. Some projects might be more demanding than others, so log your time!

READING

As writers, we hear this advice often: Read what you're writing! It's true! Read widely and often—both in and out of your comfort zone. Pick up a classic or treat yourself with the newest release. Engage in the writing world in every way.

I WANT TO BE A WRITER

Take a look at all the projects and stories you want to complete for this coming year and predict your word count for them. It's okay to fall over or under—and you may massage these as the year progresses, but throw something out there to get started. Here's a rough scope of word counts to aid you in estimation:

TYPES	GENRE
Flash Fiction 1,000 word or less	Blog Posts 200-1,200
Short Story 1,200-10,000	Romance 50,000-70,000
Novelette 10,000-30,000	Paranormal 70,000-90,000
Novella 30,000-45,000	Fantasy 90,000-120,000
Novel 50,000-85,000	Crime 90,000-100,000
Epic Novel 90,000-150,000	Mystery/Thriller/Suspense 70,000-80,000
Textbook 50,000-250,000	Memoir 30,000-70,000
Young Adult 50,000-80,000	Science Fiction 90,000-125,000
Middle Grade 25,000-40,000	Horror 70,000-100,000
Chapter Books 10,000-20,000	Historical 80,000-120,000
Picture Books 300-700	Erotica 7,000-50,000

How many words will you write this year? _____

How many words did you complete last year?_____

How many projects will you complete?_____

SET THE OFFICIAL GOAL:

WHAT WILL YOU ACCOMPLISH THIS YEAR?

Congratulations on putting your goals into writing! You're committed to the adventure ahead. You're ready. Just a few more things while we're here.

Explain your motivation right now, in this moment, in words. Why are you doing this?

_____

_____

_____

_____

What goal(s) do you want to complete this year? Complete a novel, write a dozen short stories, or land an agent? Put it into the universe!

_____

_____

_____

_____

How are you going to accomplish this writing goal? No, really, literally write down how you will do this.

_____

_____

_____

_____

When will you be writing? (*Have set times in mind so you can establish a routine, but "whenever I can" is also a valid response! Get it done in whatever way works for you and your life.*)

_____

_____

_____

_____

Where will you be writing? (*Have you tried different places?*)

_____

_____

_____

_____

What do you need in order to write successfully? (*Fluff the pillow, cue the music, pour the drink, etc.*)

_____

_____

_____

_____

How will you be writing? (*computer, laptop, yellow legal pad, quill and ink pot, etc.*)

_____

_____

_____

_____

PLAN FOR PROBLEMS

"He said we wouldn't get the treasure we seek on account of our ob-stac-les."

-Pete (Oh, Brother, Where Art Thou?)

Do some research and find writers who have experienced similar issues—what did they do to succeed? How can you use their lives/experiences as a lesson in your life?

Make a chart of obstacles that are within your control and those that are not. When you feel yourself losing momentum or focus, refer to this chart to see how you categorized the anti-writing forces in your life. If it's beyond your control, then move on; there's nothing you can do about it. Do whatever you can to get through this. But if it's something you said was controllable, think about what you can do to adjust for the issue.

What are some obstacles that prevent you from writing?

_____

How can you overcome these issues?

_____

What has prevented you from writing in the past?

_____

How will you address these known pitfalls?

DO OR DO NOT

Do you wanna die having never been to Europe? Or do you wanna go to Europe and die having been to Europe?

Why are those my only two options?

- The Spy Who Dumped Me

There is no try? Remember that you are not a jedi. Writing is not a done/not done situation—because most writers would probably agree that writing is never done, it's just due. It could always be better with one more round of edits, one more polishing session, one more gentle nudge and subtle tweak.

Writing is a process, a journey, a path deeper into the woods. Use this book to plan how far you'd like to travel along that path this year. As Tolkien said, the road goes ever on and on, and we must follow if we can.

Motivation Time!

Are you motivated by rewards or punishment?

REWARDS: ALL OF THE PRIZES!

I'm the king of the world! —Jack (Titanic)

Does the idea of a sweet prize at the end of the road get you off your phone to write? It's time to reward yourself on top of the gloating satisfaction of sweet, sweet success.

Wish List Time

You deserve all the things. Tease yourself with something really cool at the end of this road.

1st Prize

Make it worthwhile—something to motivate you when you don't want to write. A long-desired trip, a fancy meal, a new leather-bound hardcover that you don't need but really really really want...shoot for the stars in your life!

What will you do for yourself when you reach your goal?

_____

2nd Prize

This should be something cool, something you wouldn't do or get for yourself normally, but not the magical rainbow party of 1st prize. You deserve this, but you could have had that other thing—use this feeling as motivation for next time!

What will you do for yourself when you get really close to your goal?

_____

3rd Prize

Again, make this something nice, worthwhile, but not the awesomeness you listed above. For me, 3rd prize would be like Chili's—slightly special/different and fun, but definitely not what I could have been eating right now.

What will you do for yourself when you get remotely close to your goal?

_____

HONORABLE MENTION

This should be a consolation prize, the webcam you win in the office give-away, the free pedometer from your insurance company, something new, but definitely not what it could have been.

What will you do for yourself for taking the first few steps toward your goal?

ALL OF THE PUNISHMENTS!

You can't handle the truth!

-Colonel Nathan R. Jessup (A Few Good Men)

Does the idea of an awful punishment push you out of bed to do some writing? It's time to envision the reckoning waiting for you if you fail. It's Negative Reinforcement Time: You want to accomplish your goals, but sometimes you need the threat of the blade over your neck to get it done. Threaten yourself with what will happen if you do not meet your goals. (It's really important that you set realistic goals if you plan to go this route!)

I COULD HAVE TRIED HARDER

You know it's true. It wasn't life getting in the way. It wasn't beyond your control. This is totally on you. What privilege should you lose as a result? Avoid choosing something writing-related as a punishment. Make it something you really don't want to do or deal with at all.

For example, if I blow a goal because of laziness, I have to take the stairs to my office at work. I work on the third floor, and the stairs are outside in the heat. The idea of trudging up them in the heat and humidity of a Florida summer is enough to get me out of bed and in front of my computer to write every day.

What will happen if you fail this way?

PHONED IT IN

You know what happened. You were there, and you let it happen. You could have done it, but you did other things instead (not life-required things, but shiny objects that distracted you from your path). What privilege or perk should you lose? This could be something small to be a daily reminder of your failure or an all-in-one punishment that you'd rather not experience.

If I phone it in, I punish myself by wearing a really uncomfortable bra for a day or a week, depending on size of the goal/target. The discomfort is a constant reminder of my failure, motivating me the next time I think about phoning it in.

What should happen if you phone it in?

_____

_____

_____

REALLY STOPPED TRYING

You know you topped even attempting to get it done. You let the magnitude of other things get in the way, and you didn't write what you wanted. (This is a good time to sit down and think about why you failed. Check out the I Failed... Now What? section). What privilege/perk should you lose for falling off the wagon? This should be more of a punishment than the previous two, something you really don't want to happen. For me, these are usually housework-cleaning related tasks. Bonus—I'm not allowed to return to my writing until my house is spotless.

What should happen if you really stop trying?

_____

_____

_____

COMPLETELY GAVE UP

It happens. You walked away. But promises were made, and perhaps gifts were exchanged, and now you have to face the consequences. This should be serious, more than giving up your morning latte, beyond sweating over stairs or toilets. If you want the consequences method to work, this should be something you really really really don't want to experience.

Note—this isn't about berating yourself for failing, reinforcing how much you suck, or dwelling in how awful you are. Life happens. This punishment should be something you use as a proverbial sword over your neck to motivate you to write when you'd rather do anything else (even clean the toilet). My super awful worst punishment for not meeting a writing goal is living without music for an entire week. I love music—it's a huge part of my life and my makeup. I don't like a quiet house, a silent car ride, or a creepy echoing office in the evening after everyone goes home. Not having the option to cover the silence with sweet music is an awful possibility.

What should happen if you completely give up?

_____

_____

_____

Refer back to these pages periodically throughout the year. Remind yourself what you are working for—aside from the awesome, awe-inspiring feeling of finally completing a project that has haunted you for years, lingering in your brain unwritten for far too much of your life. You can totally do this!

MONTHLY PREP

Each month begins with planning—specific questions to make you think about the intersection between your writing and your life. Solid planning allows you to reach your goals.

For example, in November and December, writing time may be replaced with family time due to the holidays. It's okay to have smaller goals in the months with planned trips, scheduled events, or non-writing projects—when keeping normal routines is impossible. It's important for writers to be kind to themselves, finding that balance between accountability and self-flagellation.

LOOK AT YOUR MONTH

How many days this month will you work on writing stuff? Consider available weekdays/weekends. Will holidays affect your writing schedule? What is scheduled in your life that might affect your writing time? It's okay to plan for time when you will NOT write. Acknowledge your situation and plan accordingly.

What project(s) will you work on?

_____

_____

_____

Announcing your plan for the month is a special feeling. You can still stray if you want, but use this space to set your expectations (so you know what to prioritize this month).

What goal are you aiming to achieve?

_____

_____

_____

Now's your chance to assign a goal. Are you planning to finish a novel? Short story? Poem? Moving into the editing stage or brainstorming a new story by the end of the month? Goals can include sending out a set number of queries, gaining new followers, or buying that workbook you wanted.

What is your biggest obstacle this month?

_____

_____

_____

Anyone can look at a month and groan. Whether it's a holiday heavy month, the family reunion, or peak season with lots of overtime at your day job—we have all been there! Take a moment to acknowledge predictable obstacles.

How will you tackle these obstacles?

_____

_____

_____

Now, decide what you will do to address these issues. Will you bring a book to read and focus on a higher reading goal this month? Maybe lower your word count goal and double down on marketing since you can do social media from your phone while at a billion doctor appointments. You've got this!

What is your End of the Month reward?

_____

_____

_____

Treat yourself! It's hard following your dreams without some encouragement along the way. Life doesn't slow down, and you've made sacrifices to achieve your goals, so give yourself a pat on the back. Go to a movie, buy a new game, or even invite a friend over for wine and cheese. Always acknowledge how far you've progressed, even if not all your goals were met.

GOALS FOR THE MONTH

After this reflection time, you're ready to set your goals. It's okay to adjust them according to the demands of the month. Your monthly goals should be constantly evolving based on your previous month (that's why it's next to your Monthly Review).

WEEKLY OVERVIEW

Every week contains tasks, questions, and tips. After many painful choices, the Muses settled on what would be most helpful for your adventure this year: something to help with writer's block, remind you of your goals, and continue rewarding your creativity (perhaps with treats). Fill in this page during the week, and finish before moving on (Yes, this book has homework). Each item was chosen to prompt critical thinking and creativity on several levels.

EXERCISE

Every week, set a 5-minute timer and write a short work of fiction incorporating the two words. These short activities refill the creative well. Did you write something? Head over to the 4HP Accountable Authors Group on Facebook and share your awesome words!

QUESTIONS

WHAT WAS YOUR SPRINT TIME AND TOP WORD COUNT?

Was it a 20-minute sprint with 350 words? A 5-minute dalliance with 75 words? You're awesome! Record it here.

LIST FAVORITE (OR NEW) SONGS YOU (RE)DISCOVERED THIS WEEK:

Writers have a toolbox that inspires us. What is the soundtrack for your current project? The Researcher and the Architect both have many playlists specific to their series to keep them fueled. Often, they exchange songs!

FAVORITE FOOD OR DRINK THIS WEEK:

What yummy food and drink did you have this week? Make sure you treat yourself on occasion. The Cheerleader enjoys trying out new teas, and the Taskmaster finds ways to reward not only herself, but fellow writers. Don't assume you have to do this alone. Eat and stay healthy. Self-care is critical. Don't neglect other parts of your life!

HOW DID YOU REWARD YOURSELF?

Not all of us enjoy food as a reward, so we ask...how did you reward yourself? Did you buy that item of clothing from that store? Order something cool online? Find another new book to read? Take a short trip outside? Oh, so many options here!

WHAT PROJECT(S) DID YOU ACTUALLY WORK ON?

Pay attention to which projects you work on. Sometimes one story will flow more easily than others. That's okay! Is there a pattern? Does a certain genre speak to you more than another? Seeing how many hours you devote to a specific project can be eye-opening.

WHAT ARE YOU READING RIGHT NOW?

Write down the titles of the books you read each week. Was it a writer resource? A reference book for brainstorming? Did you reward yourself with a cozy mystery? Remember to read, exposing yourself to other writers' words.

WHAT WENT WELL/COULD IMPROVE THIS WEEK?

Time to get real. Evaluate your strengths and troubleshoot your weaknesses at least once a week.

TOTALS FOR THE WEEK

Do some math. Bust out that calculator and punch it in. How did you do? Will this keep you on track to meet your monthly/yearly goals? See your progress stack up each month. Don't discredit anything! Writing is more than laying words to the page. You're not slacking when hours are spent on other facets of being an author!

Monthly Activity Grid & Journal

Visualize where you spend your time. See how much you are doing on average and how far you've made it this year! Write down your feelings on your progress. Let it out, shout it out, and put it out there! Remind yourself how far you've made it and how far you can take it.

Monthly Review

To make it easier to find the month or circle back, we have put the month name and a color on the edge of the page. We feel it's SUPER important to look back and compare.

Questions

What was your top week this month?

There's so much that can happen in a month's time! Sit down and reflect. The Muses have pulled you into a conference room, and they're settling in to talk about how it's going (and the numbers). Don't worry—the Taskmaster is running the show, and she's already told the Researcher to focus. In fact, the Architect has pointed out some corrections while the Cheerleader is serving some tea (or coffee...or wine, depending on the month you've had).

What made your top week successful?

Looking back, it's always great to compare each week. Which one did you feel was top-notch? That's the kind of week you want to always have, one that leaves you feeling accomplished.

What made your top week successful?

What made that week so successful? Was it the reward or how you divide your time? Was there something you did differently? It's super important to be aware what made the difference so you have the ability to try to rinse and repeat.

What was your biggest obstacle?

Obstacles come in many varieties, big and small, controllable and uninvited. Acknowledge those mountains in your life and be mindful of how they influence your writing and creativity. This means you may have to change routine, maybe switch to more reading and brainstorming during these rougher climbs. It's about making your writing accountability work in your favor even in the toughest of times.

HOW DID YOU OVERCOME THIS? HOW COULD YOU IMPROVE NEXT MONTH?

Even if the answer is no, take a moment to consider strategies. Would it have been better to not worry about brainstorming and do editing or reading instead? These moments will help you tackle the next mountain.

WHAT WAS YOUR BIGGEST ACHIEVEMENT THIS MONTH?

Record the awesomeness! It can be anything and doesn't have to be something listed as a goal. Recognize what makes you feel good and boosts morale. Knowing what you can achieve makes for stronger goal setting next time.

WHAT INSPIRED YOU MOST THIS MONTH?

Inspiration comes from the most unexpected places. Track these for reference later down the road when you need a push or feel creativity slipping away. Was it a song? Something you saw in a show, movie, or documentary? Write it down! Come back to it and get recharged!

DID YOU DISCOVER A NEW WRITING TIP OR GREAT ADVICE THIS MONTH?

Writers are always learning. Advice comes in many forms, whether it's about actual writing or a fact about how to use social media in a nifty way. Write it down!

TOTAL FOR THE MONTH

Take the totals from your weeks and add those numbers up! How did you do? Did you meet a goal? Did you pass a goal? Did you not finish? These all help you plan better for the incoming month and set accurate goals.

TOTAL FOR THE YEAR

There's something satisfying about seeing how far you've come. Where are you in your journey? Do you need to adjust your weekly, monthly, or yearly goals? Don't be afraid to reassess goals. Life is unpredictable (Pandemic, anyone?). NEVER FEEL GUILTY! This is what good goal setting looks like and helps you stay on point!

Yearly Grids

In the back of this clearly amazing planner, you will find not one, but two yearly grids. These grids provide a way to visualize your achievements this year. Not only do you get to pick the colors (fancy pen time!), but you can add a handful of non-writing activities to visually compare your hobbies. At the end of the year, you can see how your time shifts to favor specific activities, especially during months with holidays or life events. A project-based grid follows this, so you can visualize how often you worked on a project, getting a sense of how much time you spent on a project.

Recognizing these habits allows you to set stronger goals and understand how to adjust when needed. Seeing how your time is spent (and perhaps how it could be better used) can be a game changer. Also, knowing how long certain types of projects take to complete lets you plan more effectively next time.

THE MUSE PAGE

We can't leave you alone. That's why every week you get a little bit of something from each muse to help you through your 7-day struggle. The content here will change up often with a combination of inspirational quotes, exercises, fun facts, writing tips, and so much more. We hope we can make you smile, take a breath, and feel inspired to keep at it. This is hard work, we know! We're writers too!

JOIN A WRITER'S COMMUNITY

First, we'd like to invite you to join the 4HP Accountable Authors Group on Facebook. There. You now have joined an author's community filled with folks who are actively trying to stay accountable! Also, there's a lot of writers communities out there. Check with your local library, colleges and universities, cafes, writing associations, and more. If you prefer online, many of these have options with a variety of hashtags on Twitter and Facebook by location and genre. Find workshops, classes, or give personal experience and advice. The greatest myth is the assumption that being a writer is a solitary ordeal. No. It's not. It doesn't have to be. Now, go into the light!

The Cheerleader

Hello! So great to meet you! I love supporting writers! If you can't tell, I'm excited to have you here and for the opportunity to be your muse. My goal is to send you positive vibes, inspire your creativity, and encourage you to reward yourself often. Let's make magic happen!

I write paranormal romance and fantasy. Favorite Book: The Talisman by Stephen King and Peter Straub.

THE ARCHITECT

Your prose is beautiful, and I'm here to help you keep it polished and publishable. We are building your writing together, so look for my advice and reminders at every turn. This is about mastering your craft, and you don't have to do it alone. Let's build a masterpiece together!

I write young adult epic fantasy and adult paranormal romance.
Favorite Book: The Blue Sword by Robin McKinley

THE RESEARCHER

Did you know... that I love to drop facts and encourage you to discover new things outside your comfort zone. Stimulating the brain and sparking creativity through research and the world around you is a vital part of being a writer. Whether we're investigating some hidden nugget of history or looking back at how strange life can be, let's light a fire on your imagination.

I write fantasy, paranormal, mythology, romance, and erotica.
Favorite Book: The Captive Prince Trilogy

THE TASKMASTER

Staying focused and on point can be difficult. Oftentimes writer's block can derail days if not months of effort. I'm here to keep you on task! One way to do this is through constant evaluation and setting goals. I will be here to create a sense of urgency while keeping you moving forward in one way or another. Now, let's get to work!

I write horror, paranormal, thriller, and erotica.
Favorite Book: "YOURS! As soon as you finish it!
Get to Work!"

Let the Accountability Planner Commence!

JANUARY

The dawn of a new year has begun, and you are about to embark on an accountability adventure only the amazing muses within this book can provide. As you start taking your first steps, remember the muses are here to encourage, educate, and eradicate any of your writing and editing woes. This about setting strong but obtainable goals and we will help you do just that!

Jan 1 - New Years
Jan 18th MLK Day

What Does Your Month Look Like

Holidays:_____ Weekends:_____
Weekdays:_____ Other:_____

What **project(s)** do you plan on working on?

_____

What **goal** are you aiming to achieve?

_____

What will be your biggest **obstacle** this month?

_____

How will you **overcome** this? Or adjust for this?

_____

What will be your End of the Month **reward**?

_____

Goals for this Month

Word Count:_____ Marketing Hours:_____
Brainstorming Hours:_____ Research Hours:_____
Editing Hours:_____ Reading Hours:_____

Week 1

JANUARY

DAILY ACCOMPLISHMENTS	**FRIDAY 1**

*Word Count:*_____   *Marketing Hours:*_____

*Brainstorming Hours:*_____   *Research Hours:*_____

*Editing Hours:*_____   *Reading Hours:*_____

DAILY ACCOMPLISHMENTS	**SATURDAY 2**

*Word Count:*_____   *Marketing Hours:*_____

*Brainstorming Hours:*_____   *Research Hours:*_____

*Editing Hours:*_____   *Reading Hours:*_____

DAILY ACCOMPLISHMENTS	**SUNDAY 3**

*Word Count:*_____   *Marketing Hours:*_____

*Brainstorming Hours:*_____   *Research Hours:*_____

*Editing Hours:*_____   *Reading Hours:*_____

DAILY ACCOMPLISHMENTS	**MONDAY 4**

*Word Count:*_____   *Marketing Hours:*_____

*Brainstorming Hours:*_____   *Research Hours:*_____

*Editing Hours:*_____   *Reading Hours:*_____

DAILY ACCOMPLISHMENTS	**TUESDAY 5**

*Word Count:*_____   *Marketing Hours:*_____

*Brainstorming Hours:*_____   *Research Hours:*_____

*Editing Hours:*_____   *Reading Hours:*_____

DAILY ACCOMPLISHMENTS	**WEDNESDAY 6**

*Word Count:*_____   *Marketing Hours:*_____

*Brainstorming Hours:*_____   *Research Hours:*_____

*Editing Hours:*_____   *Reading Hours:*_____

DAILY ACCOMPLISHMENTS	**THURSDAY 7**

*Word Count:*_____   *Marketing Hours:*_____

*Brainstorming Hours:*_____   *Research Hours:*_____

*Editing Hours:*_____   *Reading Hours:*_____

WEEKLY OVERVIEW

EXERCISE: Take 5-minute to write something with the 2 words below:

Tingle   Braid

Post your exercise on the 4HP Accountable Authors Group on Facebook!

What was your sprint time and top word count?

_____

List a new song you discovered this week:

_____

Favorite food or drink this week:

_____

How did you reward yourself?

_____

What project(s) did you work on?

_____

What are you reading?

_____

What went well this week?

_____

What could improve this week?

_____

_____

_____

TOTAL FOR THE WEEK

Word Count:_____   Marketing Hours:_____
Brainstorming Hours:_____   Research Hours:_____
Editing Hours:_____   Reading Hours:_____

Don't forget to color in your grid!

The Cheerleader

You're busy doubting yourself while some people are intimidated by your potential.

THE ARCHITECT

"The very weather can enhance the overall feel of your story and show an interesting aspect of your characters. It's all in the details you choose to show, and whose eyes you're filtering it through."

~ Susan Crandall

THE RESEARCHER

Choose one below to research. Set a timer for 20 minutes and write a story or character inspired by something you learned.
1) British "Unkillable" Soldier, Adrian Carton de Wiart
2) John "Mad Jack" Churchill

THE TASKMASTER

You have just started this journey. Put your phone down and get off of social media. You have a goal--get to it!

Week 2

DAILY ACCOMPLISHMENTS	FRIDAY 8
Word Count:	Marketing Hours:
Brainstorming Hours:	Research Hours:
Editing Hours:	Reading Hours:

DAILY ACCOMPLISHMENTS	SATURDAY 9
Word Count:	Marketing Hours:
Brainstorming Hours:	Research Hours:
Editing Hours:	Reading Hours:

DAILY ACCOMPLISHMENTS	SUNDAY 10
Word Count:	Marketing Hours:
Brainstorming Hours:	Research Hours:
Editing Hours:	Reading Hours:

DAILY ACCOMPLISHMENTS	MONDAY 11
Word Count:	Marketing Hours:
Brainstorming Hours:	Research Hours:
Editing Hours:	Reading Hours:

DAILY ACCOMPLISHMENTS	TUESDAY 12
Word Count:	Marketing Hours:
Brainstorming Hours:	Research Hours:
Editing Hours:	Reading Hours:

DAILY ACCOMPLISHMENTS	WEDNESDAY 13
Word Count:	Marketing Hours:
Brainstorming Hours:	Research Hours:
Editing Hours:	Reading Hours:

DAILY ACCOMPLISHMENTS	THURSDAY 14
Word Count:	Marketing Hours:
Brainstorming Hours:	Research Hours:
Editing Hours:	Reading Hours:

WEEKLY OVERVIEW

EXERCISE: Take 5-minute to write something with the 2 words below:

Yellow   Goat

Post your exercise on the 4HP Accountable Authors Group on Facebook!

What was your sprint time and top word count?

_____

List a new song you discovered this week:

_____

Favorite food or drink this week:

_____

How did you reward yourself?

_____

What project(s) did you work on?

_____

What are you reading?

_____

What went well this week?

_____

What could improve this week?

_____

_____

_____

TOTAL FOR THE WEEK

Word Count:_____   Marketing Hours:_____
Brainstorming Hours:_____   Research Hours:_____
Editing Hours:_____   Reading Hours:_____

Don't forget to color in your grid!

The Cheerleader

Take a moment every time you write the word "that" and read the sentence. If it still makes sense, that's one less word to edit out later!

THE ARCHITECT

Explore your settings. Many software programs, including Word and Scrivener, constantly update their grammar and spelling systems. Be sure to open and adjust those options to better fit your needs during editing.

THE RESEARCHER

Keep getting lost down a Research Rabbit Hole? No worries. Take a moment to make a DO and DON'T Want List, then focus on character, world, or plot.

THE TASKMASTER

"Never give up! Never surrender!"
~ Jason Nesmith (Galaxy Quest)

Make this quote your mantra. Keep going no matter what happens.

DAILY ACCOMPLISHMENTS   **FRIDAY 15**

WORD COUNT:_____   MARKETING HOURS:_____
BRAINSTORMING HOURS:_____   RESEARCH HOURS:_____
EDITING HOURS:_____   READING HOURS:_____

DAILY ACCOMPLISHMENTS   **SATURDAY 16**

WORD COUNT:_____   MARKETING HOURS:_____
BRAINSTORMING HOURS:_____   RESEARCH HOURS:_____
EDITING HOURS:_____   READING HOURS:_____

DAILY ACCOMPLISHMENTS   **SUNDAY 17**

WORD COUNT:_____   MARKETING HOURS:_____
BRAINSTORMING HOURS:_____   RESEARCH HOURS:_____
EDITING HOURS:_____   READING HOURS:_____

DAILY ACCOMPLISHMENTS   **MONDAY 18**

WORD COUNT:_____   MARKETING HOURS:_____
BRAINSTORMING HOURS:_____   RESEARCH HOURS:_____
EDITING HOURS:_____   READING HOURS:_____

DAILY ACCOMPLISHMENTS   **TUESDAY 19**

WORD COUNT:_____   MARKETING HOURS:_____
BRAINSTORMING HOURS:_____   RESEARCH HOURS:_____
EDITING HOURS:_____   READING HOURS:_____

DAILY ACCOMPLISHMENTS   **WEDNESDAY 20**

WORD COUNT:_____   MARKETING HOURS:_____
BRAINSTORMING HOURS:_____   RESEARCH HOURS:_____
EDITING HOURS:_____   READING HOURS:_____

DAILY ACCOMPLISHMENTS   **THURSDAY 21**

WORD COUNT:_____   MARKETING HOURS:_____
BRAINSTORMING HOURS:_____   RESEARCH HOURS:_____
EDITING HOURS:_____   READING HOURS:_____

JANUARY

Weekly Overview

Exercise: Take 5-minute to write something with the 2 words below:

Light   Turnip

Post your exercise on the 4HP Accountable Authors Group on Facebook!

What was your sprint time and top word count?

_____

List a new song you discovered this week:

_____

Favorite food or drink this week:

_____

How did you reward yourself?

_____

What project(s) did you work on?

_____

What are you reading?

_____

What went well this week?

_____

What could improve this week?

_____

_____

_____

Total for the Week

Word Count:_____   Marketing Hours:_____

Brainstorming Hours:_____   Research Hours:_____

Editing Hours:_____   Reading Hours:_____

Don't forget to color in your grid!

The Cheerleader

What's your favorite book of all time? Why?

THE ARCHITECT

Editing got you down?
Try editing someone else's work or short
story. This is a great way to
stretch your muscles without
the fog of fretting over your
own prose.

THE RESEARCHER

Etymology for the word *Concubine* derives from the masculine Latin word *concubina*. Around the time it started, Rome was founded with a 12:1 ration of men to women... hmm...

THE TASKMASTER

"If you want to change the world, pick up your pen and write."

~ Martin Luther King

Right now is your chance to change the world. I know you are up to the task.

Week 4

Daily Accomplishments   **Friday 22**

Word Count:_____   Marketing Hours:_____
Brainstorming Hours:_____   Research Hours:_____
Editing Hours:_____   Reading Hours:_____

Daily Accomplishments   **Saturday 23**

Word Count:_____   Marketing Hours:_____
Brainstorming Hours:_____   Research Hours:_____
Editing Hours:_____   Reading Hours:_____

Daily Accomplishments   **Sunday 24**

Word Count:_____   Marketing Hours:_____
Brainstorming Hours:_____   Research Hours:_____
Editing Hours:_____   Reading Hours:_____

Daily Accomplishments   **Monday 25**

Word Count:_____   Marketing Hours:_____
Brainstorming Hours:_____   Research Hours:_____
Editing Hours:_____   Reading Hours:_____

Daily Accomplishments   **Tuesday 26**

Word Count:_____   Marketing Hours:_____
Brainstorming Hours:_____   Research Hours:_____
Editing Hours:_____   Reading Hours:_____

Daily Accomplishments   **Wednesday 27**

Word Count:_____   Marketing Hours:_____
Brainstorming Hours:_____   Research Hours:_____
Editing Hours:_____   Reading Hours:_____

Daily Accomplishments   **Thursday 28**

Word Count:_____   Marketing Hours:_____
Brainstorming Hours:_____   Research Hours:_____
Editing Hours:_____   Reading Hours:_____

JANUARY

WEEKLY OVERVIEW

EXERCISE: Take 5-minute to write something with the 2 words below:

Barn   Frog

Post your exercise on the 4HP Accountable Authors Group on Facebook!

What was your sprint time and top word count?

_____

List a new song you discovered this week:

_____

Favorite food or drink this week:

_____

How did you reward yourself?

_____

What project(s) did you work on?

_____

What are you reading?

_____

What went well this week?

_____

What could improve this week?

_____

_____

_____

TOTAL FOR THE WEEK

Word Count:_____   Marketing Hours:_____
Brainstorming Hours:_____   Research Hours:_____
Editing Hours:_____   Reading Hours:_____

Don't forget to color in your grid!

The Cheerleader

What motivates your writing? Make a list of things that excite you. Use this to fuel your writing and increase your word count.

THE ARCHITECT

Search for filter words: "She saw, she heard, she noticed, etc." Then try to eliminate them as much as you can.

THE RESEARCHER

"Motivation is what gets you started. Habit is what keeps you going."

~ Jim Ryan

THE TASKMASTER

When did you last change your author photo or background image on social media? Do it now!

DAILY ACCOMPLISHMENTS	**FRIDAY 29**
*Word Count:*_____	*Marketing Hours:*_____
*Brainstorming Hours:*_____	*Research Hours:*_____
*Editing Hours:*_____	*Reading Hours:*_____

DAILY ACCOMPLISHMENTS	**SATURDAY 30**
*Word Count:*_____	*Marketing Hours:*_____
*Brainstorming Hours:*_____	*Research Hours:*_____
*Editing Hours:*_____	*Reading Hours:*_____

DAILY ACCOMPLISHMENTS	**SUNDAY 31**
*Word Count:*_____	*Marketing Hours:*_____
*Brainstorming Hours:*_____	*Research Hours:*_____
*Editing Hours:*_____	*Reading Hours:*_____

THE TASKMASTER

It is the start of your epic adventure. You may be feeling a little nervous, a bit excited, and most especially, certain you are going to rule the world by the end of 2021. Remember, you can be your own worst enemy. Get out of your own way.

JANUARY

Weekly Overview

Ray   Almond

Post your exercise on the 4HP Accountable Authors Group on Facebook!

What was your sprint time and top word count?

_____

List a new song you discovered this week:

_____

Favorite food or drink this week:

_____

How did you reward yourself?

_____

What project(s) did you work on?

_____

What are you reading?

_____

What went well this week?

_____

What could improve this week?

_____

_____

_____

Total for the Week

Word Count:_____   Marketing Hours:_____
Brainstorming Hours:_____   Research Hours:_____
Editing Hours:_____   Reading Hours:_____

Don't forget to color in your grid!

MONTHLY ACTIVITY GRID

WRITING OR WORD COUNT	1
BRAINSTORMING	
EDITING	
MARKETING OR SOCIAL MEDIA	
RESEARCH	
READING	
OTHER:	

JANUARY

YOUR AVERAGE WORD COUNT FOR THE MONTH

Total Word Count:_____ Divided by _____ days =_____

TOTAL FOR THE YEAR SO FAR

Word Count:_____   Marketing Hours:_____
Brainstorming Hours:_____   Research Hours:_____
Editing Hours:_____   Reading Hours:_____

JOURNAL

What was your **top week**?

_____

What made your **top week** successful?

_____

What was your biggest **obstacle**?

_____

How did you **overcome** this? Or could do better next time?

_____

_____

What was your biggest **achievement**?

_____

_____

What **inspired** you most this month?

_____

Did you **discover** a new writing tip or advice this month?

_____

_____

TOTAL FOR THE MONTH

Word Count:_____   Research Hours:_____
Brainstorming Hours:_____   Reading Hours:_____
Editing Hours:_____
Marketing Hours:_____

TOTAL FOR THE YEAR SO FAR

Word Count:_____   Research Hours:_____
Brainstorming Hours:_____   Reading Hours:_____
Editing Hours:_____
Marketing Hours:_____

Don't forget to color in your grid!

February

As you begin month two of this adventure, you should start to find your routine. Experts say it takes six weeks to develop a habit. Do not forget that this is your journey, and February is the month of love. Make sure you are loving yourself!

Feb 15 -President's Day

What Does Your Month Look Like

Holidays:_____   Weekends:_____
Weekdays:_____   Other:_____

What **project(s)** do you plan on working on?

_____

What **goal** are you aiming to achieve?

_____

What will be your biggest **obstacle** this month?

_____

How will you **overcome** this? Or adjust for this?

_____

What will be your End of the Month **reward**?

_____

Goals for this Month

Word Count:_____   Marketing Hours:_____
Brainstorming Hours:_____   Research Hours:_____
Editing Hours:_____   Reading Hours:_____

23

WEEK 1

DAILY ACCOMPLISHMENTS   **MONDAY 1**

Word Count: _____
Brainstorming Hours: _____
Editing Hours: _____

Marketing Hours: _____
Research Hours: _____
Reading Hours: _____

DAILY ACCOMPLISHMENTS   **TUESDAY 2**

Word Count: _____
Brainstorming Hours: _____
Editing Hours: _____

Marketing Hours: _____
Research Hours: _____
Reading Hours: _____

DAILY ACCOMPLISHMENTS   **WEDNESDAY 3**

Word Count: _____
Brainstorming Hours: _____
Editing Hours: _____

Marketing Hours: _____
Research Hours: _____
Reading Hours: _____

DAILY ACCOMPLISHMENTS   **THURSDAY 4**

Word Count: _____
Brainstorming Hours: _____
Editing Hours: _____

Marketing Hours: _____
Research Hours: _____
Reading Hours: _____

DAILY ACCOMPLISHMENTS   **FRIDAY 5**

Word Count: _____
Brainstorming Hours: _____
Editing Hours: _____

Marketing Hours: _____
Research Hours: _____
Reading Hours: _____

DAILY ACCOMPLISHMENTS   **SATURDAY 6**

Word Count: _____
Brainstorming Hours: _____
Editing Hours: _____

Marketing Hours: _____
Research Hours: _____
Reading Hours: _____

DAILY ACCOMPLISHMENTS   **SUNDAY 7**

Word Count: _____
Brainstorming Hours: _____
Editing Hours: _____

Marketing Hours: _____
Research Hours: _____
Reading Hours: _____

WEEKLY OVERVIEW

EXERCISE: Take 5-minute to write something with the 2 words below:

Pink   Turtle

Post your exercise on the 4HP Accountable Authors Group on Facebook!

What was your sprint time and top word count?

_____

List a new song you discovered this week:

_____

Favorite food or drink this week:

_____

How did you reward yourself?

_____

What project(s) did you work on?

_____

What are you reading?

_____

What went well this week?

_____

What could improve this week?

_____

_____

_____

TOTAL FOR THE WEEK

Word Count:_____   Marketing Hours:_____
Brainstorming Hours:_____   Research Hours:_____
Editing Hours:_____   Reading Hours:_____

Don't forget to color in your grid!

The Cheerleader

"When you realize you want to spend the rest of your life with somebody, you want the rest of your life to start as soon as possible."

~ Harry Burns (When Harry Met Sally)

THE ARCHITECT

Blurb Time: Revisit the blurb for your current project.

Does this still work?

☐ Yes! It works!

☐ No, I need to work on this some more!

THE RESEARCHER

Use comments as notes for your future self. Add thoughts if you are stuck.
Or to make sure you counted the right number of bullets to reload that gun.

THE TASKMASTER

Strike a balance between showing and telling. Unless you're writing a book about trees, or it's a vital detail to the story, nobody cares about three paragraphs describing the shape of a leaf. Find this crap and remove it. (Tolkien has strong feelings about this.)

FEBRUARY

DAILY ACCOMPLISHMENTS   MONDAY 8

Word Count: _____   *Marketing Hours:* _____

Brainstorming Hours: _____   *Research Hours:* _____

Editing Hours: _____   *Reading Hours:* _____

DAILY ACCOMPLISHMENTS   TUESDAY 9

Word Count: _____   *Marketing Hours:* _____

Brainstorming Hours: _____   *Research Hours:* _____

Editing Hours: _____   *Reading Hours:* _____

DAILY ACCOMPLISHMENTS   WEDNESDAY 10

Word Count: _____   *Marketing Hours:* _____

Brainstorming Hours: _____   *Research Hours:* _____

Editing Hours: _____   *Reading Hours:* _____

DAILY ACCOMPLISHMENTS   THURSDAY 11

Word Count: _____   *Marketing Hours:* _____

Brainstorming Hours: _____   *Research Hours:* _____

Editing Hours: _____   *Reading Hours:* _____

DAILY ACCOMPLISHMENTS   FRIDAY 12

Word Count: _____   *Marketing Hours:* _____

Brainstorming Hours: _____   *Research Hours:* _____

Editing Hours: _____   *Reading Hours:* _____

DAILY ACCOMPLISHMENTS   SATURDAY 13

Word Count: _____   *Marketing Hours:* _____

Brainstorming Hours: _____   *Research Hours:* _____

Editing Hours: _____   *Reading Hours:* _____

DAILY ACCOMPLISHMENTS   SUNDAY 14

Word Count: _____   *Marketing Hours:* _____

Brainstorming Hours: _____   *Research Hours:* _____

Editing Hours: _____   *Reading Hours:* _____

WEEKLY OVERVIEW

EXERCISE: Take 5-minute to write something with the 2 words below:

Dream   Peanut

Post your exercise on the 4HP Accountable Authors Group on Facebook!

What was your sprint time and top word count?

_____

List a new song you discovered this week:

_____

Favorite food or drink this week:

_____

How did you reward yourself?

_____

What project(s) did you work on?

_____

What are you reading?

_____

What went well this week?

_____

What could improve this week?

_____

_____

_____

TOTAL FOR THE WEEK

Word Count:_____   Marketing Hours:_____
Brainstorming Hours:_____   Research Hours:_____
Editing Hours:_____   Reading Hours:_____

Don't forget to color in your grid!

FEBRUARY

The Cheerleader

Make a list of *"Never have I ever"* items that you wish to accomplish as a writer.

THE ARCHITECT

Use dolls to act out fighting scenes *(or even sex scenes)* to ensure body parts are in the right places.

THE RESEARCHER

Boxers, briefs, or banana hammocks? Discuss.

THE TASKMASTER

"It's the job that's never started that takes the longest to finish."

~ Samwise Gamgee (Lord of the Rings)

You need to be writing every single day, even if it is only for 20 minutes.

FEBRUARY

FEBRUARY

DAILY ACCOMPLISHMENTS	MONDAY 15
WORD COUNT:	MARKETING HOURS:
BRAINSTORMING HOURS:	RESEARCH HOURS:
EDITING HOURS:	READING HOURS:

DAILY ACCOMPLISHMENTS	TUESDAY 16
WORD COUNT:	MARKETING HOURS:
BRAINSTORMING HOURS:	RESEARCH HOURS:
EDITING HOURS:	READING HOURS:

DAILY ACCOMPLISHMENTS	WEDNESDAY 17
WORD COUNT:	MARKETING HOURS:
BRAINSTORMING HOURS:	RESEARCH HOURS:
EDITING HOURS:	READING HOURS:

DAILY ACCOMPLISHMENTS	THURSDAY 18
WORD COUNT:	MARKETING HOURS:
BRAINSTORMING HOURS:	RESEARCH HOURS:
EDITING HOURS:	READING HOURS:

DAILY ACCOMPLISHMENTS	FRIDAY 19
WORD COUNT:	MARKETING HOURS:
BRAINSTORMING HOURS:	RESEARCH HOURS:
EDITING HOURS:	READING HOURS:

DAILY ACCOMPLISHMENTS	SATURDAY 20
WORD COUNT:	MARKETING HOURS:
BRAINSTORMING HOURS:	RESEARCH HOURS:
EDITING HOURS:	READING HOURS:

DAILY ACCOMPLISHMENTS	SUNDAY 21
WORD COUNT:	MARKETING HOURS:
BRAINSTORMING HOURS:	RESEARCH HOURS:
EDITING HOURS:	READING HOURS:

Weekly Overview

EXERCISE: Take 5-minute to write something with the 2 words below:

Movie   Tumble

Post your exercise on the 4HP Accountable Authors Group on Facebook!

What was your sprint time and top word count?

_____

List a new song you discovered this week:

_____

Favorite food or drink this week:

_____

How did you reward yourself?

_____

What project(s) did you work on?

_____

What are you reading?

_____

What went well this week?

_____

What could improve this week?

_____

_____

_____

TOTAL FOR THE WEEK

Word Count:_____   Marketing Hours:_____
Brainstorming Hours:_____   Research Hours:_____
Editing Hours:_____   Reading Hours:_____

Don't forget to color in your grid!

The Cheerleader

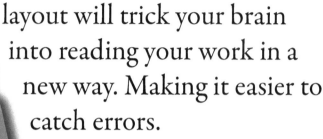

Print out your work in a different font and size during revisions. The new layout will trick your brain into reading your work in a new way. Making it easier to catch errors.

THE ARCHITECT

"Beautiful writing isn't about the words we use. It's about the emotions we evoke."

~ Katie Ganshert

THE RESEARCHER

5 Minute Outline Break:
Outline a project that
you're thinking about.
Set a timer.
GO!

THE TASKMASTER

Sit your butt in a chair and write!
This isn't a request.
It's a requirement.

FEBRUARY

Week 4

DAILY ACCOMPLISHMENTS   **MONDAY 22**

Word Count:_____   Marketing Hours:_____
Brainstorming Hours:_____   Research Hours:_____
Editing Hours:_____   Reading Hours:_____

DAILY ACCOMPLISHMENTS   **TUESDAY 23**

Word Count:_____   Marketing Hours:_____
Brainstorming Hours:_____   Research Hours:_____
Editing Hours:_____   Reading Hours:_____

DAILY ACCOMPLISHMENTS   **WEDNESDAY 24**

Word Count:_____   Marketing Hours:_____
Brainstorming Hours:_____   Research Hours:_____
Editing Hours:_____   Reading Hours:_____

DAILY ACCOMPLISHMENTS   **THURSDAY 25**

Word Count:_____   Marketing Hours:_____
Brainstorming Hours:_____   Research Hours:_____
Editing Hours:_____   Reading Hours:_____

DAILY ACCOMPLISHMENTS   **FRIDAY 26**

Word Count:_____   Marketing Hours:_____
Brainstorming Hours:_____   Research Hours:_____
Editing Hours:_____   Reading Hours:_____

DAILY ACCOMPLISHMENTS   **SATURDAY 27**

Word Count:_____   Marketing Hours:_____
Brainstorming Hours:_____   Research Hours:_____
Editing Hours:_____   Reading Hours:_____

DAILY ACCOMPLISHMENTS   **SUNDAY 28**

Word Count:_____   Marketing Hours:_____
Brainstorming Hours:_____   Research Hours:_____
Editing Hours:_____   Reading Hours:_____

Weekly Overview

EXERCISE: Take 5-minute to write something with the 2 words below:

Fountain   Cutain

Post your exercise on the 4HP Accountable Authors Group on Facebook!

What was your sprint time and top word count?

_____

List a new song you discovered this week:

_____

Favorite food or drink this week:

_____

How did you reward yourself?

_____

What project(s) did you work on?

_____

What are you reading?

_____

What went well this week?

_____

What could improve this week?

_____

_____

_____

Total for the Week

Word Count:_____   Marketing Hours:_____
Brainstorming Hours:_____   Research Hours:_____
Editing Hours:_____   Reading Hours:_____

Don't forget to color in your grid!

The Cheerleader

Find a book outside of your comfort zone.
Give it a try!
Support your local library!

THE ARCHITECT

Plot Holes Everywhere:
What plot issues are you struggling with right now? Jot down possible stopgaps to explain the events.

THE RESEARCHER

"Writing, to me, is simply thinking through my fingers."

~ Isaac Asimov

THE TASKMASTER

Have you written a review for the last book you read? If not, do that now.

FEBRUARY

39

MONTHLY ACTIVITY GRID

WRITING OR WORD COUNT	
BRAINSTORMING	
EDITING	
MARKETING OR SOCIAL MEDIA	
RESEARCH	
READING	
OTHER:	

FEBRUARY

1 2 3 4 5 6 7 8 9 10 11 12 13 14 15 16 17 18 19 20 21 22 23 24 25 26 27 28 29 30 31

YOUR AVERAGE WORD COUNT FOR THE MONTH

Total Word Count:_____ Divided by _____ days =_____

TOTAL FOR THE YEAR SO FAR

Word Count:_____   Marketing Hours:_____
Brainstorming Hours:_____   Research Hours:_____
Editing Hours:_____   Reading Hours:_____

JOURNAL

What was your **top week**?

_____

What made your **top week** successful?

_____

What was your biggest **obstacle**?

_____

How did you **overcome** this? Or could do better next time?

_____

_____

What was your biggest **achievement**?

_____

_____

What **inspired** you most this month?

_____

Did you **discover** a new writing tip or advice this month?

_____

_____

TOTAL FOR THE MONTH

Word Count:_____   Research Hours:_____
Brainstorming Hours:_____   Reading Hours:_____
Editing Hours:_____
Marketing Hours:_____

TOTAL FOR THE YEAR SO FAR

Word Count:_____   Research Hours:_____
Brainstorming Hours:_____   Reading Hours:_____
Editing Hours:_____
Marketing Hours:_____

Don't forget to color in your grid!

MARCH

Now is the time to establish your luck for this month. If you do not see a rainbow, create it. You decide on your version of the pot of gold, but be sure to set your goals so that you can succeed. Don't forget that you can join the 4HP Accountable Authors group on Facebook and find people just like you to collaborate with. Good luck, Fellow Author!

Spring Break

WHAT DOES YOUR MONTH LOOK LIKE

Holidays:_____   Weekends:_____
Weekdays:_____   Other:_____

What **project(s)** do you plan on working on?

_____

What **goal** are you aiming to achieve?

_____

What will be your biggest **obstacle** this month?

_____

How will you **overcome** this? Or adjust for this?

_____

What will be your End of the Month **reward**?

_____

GOALS FOR THIS MONTH

Word Count:_____   Marketing Hours:_____
Brainstorming Hours:_____   Research Hours:_____
Editing Hours:_____   Reading Hours:_____

WEEK 1

DAILY ACCOMPLISHMENTS	MONDAY 1
Word Count:	*Marketing Hours:*
Brainstorming Hours:	*Research Hours:*
Editing Hours:	*Reading Hours:*

DAILY ACCOMPLISHMENTS	TUESDAY 2
Word Count:	*Marketing Hours:*
Brainstorming Hours:	*Research Hours:*
Editing Hours:	*Reading Hours:*

DAILY ACCOMPLISHMENTS	WEDNESDAY 3
Word Count:	*Marketing Hours:*
Brainstorming Hours:	*Research Hours:*
Editing Hours:	*Reading Hours:*

DAILY ACCOMPLISHMENTS	THURSDAY 4
Word Count:	*Marketing Hours:*
Brainstorming Hours:	*Research Hours:*
Editing Hours:	*Reading Hours:*

DAILY ACCOMPLISHMENTS	FRIDAY 5
Word Count:	*Marketing Hours:*
Brainstorming Hours:	*Research Hours:*
Editing Hours:	*Reading Hours:*

DAILY ACCOMPLISHMENTS	SATURDAY 6
Word Count:	*Marketing Hours:*
Brainstorming Hours:	*Research Hours:*
Editing Hours:	*Reading Hours:*

DAILY ACCOMPLISHMENTS	SUNDAY 7
Word Count:	*Marketing Hours:*
Brainstorming Hours:	*Research Hours:*
Editing Hours:	*Reading Hours:*

MARCH

Weekly Overview

EXERCISE: Take 5-minute to write something with the 2 words below:

Apple   Wind

Post your exercise on the 4HP Accountable Authors Group on Facebook!

What was your sprint time and top word count?

_____

List a new song you discovered this week:

_____

Favorite food or drink this week:

_____

How did you reward yourself?

_____

What project(s) did you work on?

_____

What are you reading?

_____

What went well this week?

_____

What could improve this week?

_____

_____

_____

Total for the Week

Word Count:_____   Marketing Hours:_____
Brainstorming Hours:_____   Research Hours:_____
Editing Hours:_____   Reading Hours:_____

Don't forget to color in your grid!

MARCH

The Cheerleader

Name the last genre book you read that's similar to your current project.

THE ARCHITECT

"It is perfectly okay to write garbage - as long as you edit it brillantly."

~ C.J. Cherryh

THE RESEARCHER

Use maps, photos, and even Google Earth to get a sense of places you've never visited before writing about them. You don't want to miss a vital detail about the landscape.

THE TASKMASTER

Pitch your book in 30 seconds or less. Say it out loud. Can you do it? If not, practice in front of a mirror or to another person. It's important to memorize this speech.

MARCH

DAILY ACCOMPLISHMENTS   **MONDAY 8**

Word Count: _____
Brainstorming Hours: _____
Editing Hours: _____

Marketing Hours: _____
Research Hours: _____
Reading Hours: _____

DAILY ACCOMPLISHMENTS   **TUESDAY 9**

Word Count: _____
Brainstorming Hours: _____
Editing Hours: _____

Marketing Hours: _____
Research Hours: _____
Reading Hours: _____

DAILY ACCOMPLISHMENTS   **WEDNESDAY 10**

Word Count: _____
Brainstorming Hours: _____
Editing Hours: _____

Marketing Hours: _____
Research Hours: _____
Reading Hours: _____

DAILY ACCOMPLISHMENTS   **THURSDAY 11**

Word Count: _____
Brainstorming Hours: _____
Editing Hours: _____

Marketing Hours: _____
Research Hours: _____
Reading Hours: _____

DAILY ACCOMPLISHMENTS   **FRIDAY 12**

Word Count: _____
Brainstorming Hours: _____
Editing Hours: _____

Marketing Hours: _____
Research Hours: _____
Reading Hours: _____

DAILY ACCOMPLISHMENTS   **SATURDAY 13**

Word Count: _____
Brainstorming Hours: _____
Editing Hours: _____

Marketing Hours: _____
Research Hours: _____
Reading Hours: _____

DAILY ACCOMPLISHMENTS   **SUNDAY 14**

Word Count: _____
Brainstorming Hours: _____
Editing Hours: _____

Marketing Hours: _____
Research Hours: _____
Reading Hours: _____

MARCH

Weekly Overview

EXERCISE: Take 5-minute to write something with the 2 words below:

Shiver   Tulip

Post your exercise on the 4HP Accountable Authors Group on Facebook!

What was your sprint time and top word count?

_____

List a new song you discovered this week:

_____

Favorite food or drink this week:

_____

How did you reward yourself?

_____

What project(s) did you work on?

_____

What are you reading?

_____

What went well this week?

_____

What could improve this week?

_____

_____

_____

Total for the Week

Word Count:_____   Marketing Hours:_____
Brainstorming Hours:_____   Research Hours:_____
Editing Hours:_____   Reading Hours:_____

Don't forget to color in your grid!

MARCH

The Cheerleader

"A non-writing writer is a monster courting insanity."

~ Franz Kafka

THE ARCHITECT

Do you keep notes about your charaters?
Make sure to track details about them and their relationships.

THE RESEARCHER

Interview Time:
What questions would
offend or upset your
character? Why?

THE TASKMASTER

You can be your worst
critic (*enemy*).
STOP IT!!!
You're awesome.
I believe in you.

MARCH

Week 3

DAILY ACCOMPLISHMENTS   **MONDAY 15**

WORD COUNT:_____   MARKETING HOURS:_____
BRAINSTORMING HOURS:_____   RESEARCH HOURS:_____
EDITING HOURS:_____   READING HOURS:_____

DAILY ACCOMPLISHMENTS   **TUESDAY 16**

WORD COUNT:_____   MARKETING HOURS:_____
BRAINSTORMING HOURS:_____   RESEARCH HOURS:_____
EDITING HOURS:_____   READING HOURS:_____

DAILY ACCOMPLISHMENTS   **WEDNESDAY 17**

WORD COUNT:_____   MARKETING HOURS:_____
BRAINSTORMING HOURS:_____   RESEARCH HOURS:_____
EDITING HOURS:_____   READING HOURS:_____

DAILY ACCOMPLISHMENTS   **THURSDAY 18**

WORD COUNT:_____   MARKETING HOURS:_____
BRAINSTORMING HOURS:_____   RESEARCH HOURS:_____
EDITING HOURS:_____   READING HOURS:_____

DAILY ACCOMPLISHMENTS   **FRIDAY 19**

WORD COUNT:_____   MARKETING HOURS:_____
BRAINSTORMING HOURS:_____   RESEARCH HOURS:_____
EDITING HOURS:_____   READING HOURS:_____

DAILY ACCOMPLISHMENTS   **SATURDAY 20**

WORD COUNT:_____   MARKETING HOURS:_____
BRAINSTORMING HOURS:_____   RESEARCH HOURS:_____
EDITING HOURS:_____   READING HOURS:_____

DAILY ACCOMPLISHMENTS   **SUNDAY 21**

WORD COUNT:_____   MARKETING HOURS:_____
BRAINSTORMING HOURS:_____   RESEARCH HOURS:_____
EDITING HOURS:_____   READING HOURS:_____

WEEKLY OVERVIEW

EXERCISE: Take 5-minute to write something with the 2 words below:

Heart   Cork

Post your exercise on the 4HP Accountable Authors Group on Facebook!

What was your sprint time and top word count?

_____

List a new song you discovered this week:

_____

Favorite food or drink this week:

_____

How did you reward yourself?

_____

What project(s) did you work on?

_____

What are you reading?

_____

What went well this week?

_____

What could improve this week?

_____

_____

_____

TOTAL FOR THE WEEK

Word Count:_____   Marketing Hours:_____
Brainstorming Hours:_____   Research Hours:_____
Editing Hours:_____   Reading Hours:_____

Don't forget to color in your grid!

The Cheerleader

Write at a different time once this week.
How did it go?

THE ARCHITECT

Read widely and often.
It's a great way to build your
internal editor.

THE RESEARCHER

Aliens. UFOs. Do you believe?

☐ Yes   ☐ No

Does your character believe?

☐ Yes   ☐ No

Why or why not?

THE TASKMASTER

"You don't have to be great to start, but you have to start to be great."

~ Zig Ziglar

Are you maintaining your monthly goals? You're in control of that. Treat this with the same passion you want your readers to feel about your work.

MARCH

WEEK 4

DAILY ACCOMPLISHMENTS	MONDAY 22
WORD COUNT:	MARKETING HOURS:
BRAINSTORMING HOURS:	RESEARCH HOURS:
EDITING HOURS:	READING HOURS:

DAILY ACCOMPLISHMENTS	TUESDAY 23
WORD COUNT:	MARKETING HOURS:
BRAINSTORMING HOURS:	RESEARCH HOURS:
EDITING HOURS:	READING HOURS:

DAILY ACCOMPLISHMENTS	WEDNESDAY 24
WORD COUNT:	MARKETING HOURS:
BRAINSTORMING HOURS:	RESEARCH HOURS:
EDITING HOURS:	READING HOURS:

DAILY ACCOMPLISHMENTS	THURSDAY 25
WORD COUNT:	MARKETING HOURS:
BRAINSTORMING HOURS:	RESEARCH HOURS:
EDITING HOURS:	READING HOURS:

DAILY ACCOMPLISHMENTS	FRIDAY 26
WORD COUNT:	MARKETING HOURS:
BRAINSTORMING HOURS:	RESEARCH HOURS:
EDITING HOURS:	READING HOURS:

DAILY ACCOMPLISHMENTS	SATURDAY 27
WORD COUNT:	MARKETING HOURS:
BRAINSTORMING HOURS:	RESEARCH HOURS:
EDITING HOURS:	READING HOURS:

DAILY ACCOMPLISHMENTS	SUNDAY 28
WORD COUNT:	MARKETING HOURS:
BRAINSTORMING HOURS:	RESEARCH HOURS:
EDITING HOURS:	READING HOURS:

Weekly Overview

EXERCISE: Take 5-minute to write something with the 2 words below:

Pin   Ticket

Post your exercise on the 4HP Accountable Authors Group on Facebook!

What was your sprint time and top word count?

_____

List a new song you discovered this week:

_____

Favorite food or drink this week:

_____

How did you reward yourself?

_____

What project(s) did you work on?

_____

What are you reading?

_____

What went well this week?

_____

What could improve this week?

_____

_____

_____

Total for the Week

Word Count:_____   Marketing Hours:_____
Brainstorming Hours:_____   Research Hours:_____
Editing Hours:_____   Reading Hours:_____

Don't forget to color in your grid!

The Cheerleader

Write in a different place once this week. How did it go?

THE ARCHITECT

"We write because we believe the human spirit cannot be tamed and should not be trained."

~ *Nikki Giovanni*

THE RESEARCHER

Have you started your worldbook? Even if you're writing in modern times, keep track of your characters by creating a reference guide.

THE TASKMASTER

Pick up or discover a new book on writing. Find stronger word choices, master character dialogue, or add depth to worldbuilding and plot.

MARCH

DAILY ACCOMPLISHMENTS	MONDAY 29
*Word Count:*_____	*Marketing Hours:*_____
*Brainstorming Hours:*_____	*Research Hours:*_____
*Editing Hours:*_____	*Reading Hours:*_____

DAILY ACCOMPLISHMENTS	TUESDAY 30
*Word Count:*_____	*Marketing Hours:*_____
*Brainstorming Hours:*_____	*Research Hours:*_____
*Editing Hours:*_____	*Reading Hours:*_____

DAILY ACCOMPLISHMENTS	WEDNESDAY 31
*Word Count:*_____	*Marketing Hours:*_____
*Brainstorming Hours:*_____	*Research Hours:*_____
*Editing Hours:*_____	*Reading Hours:*_____

The Cheerleader

"Perfectionism is the voice of the oppressor, the enemy of the people. It will keep you cramped and insane your whole life, and it is the main obstacle between you and a shitty first draft. I think perfectionism is based on the obsessive belief that if you run carefully enough, hitting each stepping-stone just right, you won't have to die. The truth is that you will die anyway and that a lot of people who aren't even looking at their feet are going to do a whole lot better than you, and have a lot more fun while they're doing it."

-Anne Lamott (Bird by Bird: Some Instructions on Writing and Life)

MARCH

WEEKLY OVERVIEW

EXERCISE: Take 5-minute to write something with the 2 words below:

Struggle   Fresh

Post your exercise on the 4HP Accountable Authors Group on Facebook!

What was your sprint time and top word count?

_____

List a new song you discovered this week:

_____

Favorite food or drink this week:

_____

How did you reward yourself?

_____

What project(s) did you work on?

_____

What are you reading?

_____

What went well this week?

_____

What could improve this week?

_____

_____

_____

TOTAL FOR THE WEEK

Word Count:_____   Marketing Hours:_____
Brainstorming Hours:_____   Research Hours:_____
Editing Hours:_____   Reading Hours:_____

Don't forget to color in your grid!

MONTHLY ACTIVITY GRID

MARCH

WRITING OR WORD COUNT	
BRAINSTORMING	
EDITING	
MARKETING OR SOCIAL MEDIA	
RESEARCH	
READING	
OTHER:	

1 2 3 4 5 6 7 8 9 10 11 12 13 14 15 16 17 18 19 20 21 22 23 24 25 26 27 28 29 30 31

YOUR AVERAGE WORD COUNT FOR THE MONTH

Total Word Count:_____ Divided by _____ days =_____

TOTAL FOR THE YEAR SO FAR

Word Count:_____   Marketing Hours:_____
Brainstorming Hours:_____   Research Hours:_____
Editing Hours:_____   Reading Hours:_____

JOURNAL

MARCH

What was your **top week**?

_____

What made your **top week** successful?

_____

What was your biggest **obstacle**?

_____

How did you **overcome** this? Or could do better next time?

_____

_____

What was your biggest **achievement**?

_____

_____

What **inspired** you most this month?

_____

Did you **discover** a new writing tip or advice this month?

_____

_____

TOTAL FOR THE MONTH

Word Count:_____   Research Hours:_____
Brainstorming Hours:_____   Reading Hours:_____
Editing Hours:_____
Marketing Hours:_____

TOTAL FOR THE YEAR SO FAR

Word Count:_____   Research Hours:_____
Brainstorming Hours:_____   Reading Hours:_____
Editing Hours:_____
Marketing Hours:_____

Don't forget to color in your grid!

APRIL

April is a month of new beginings. Spring is in full swing, and new animals emerge into the world. Make sure you take some time to step outside and see the world blooming around you. Who knows who or what you might encounter outside your door?

April 4 - Easter

WHAT DOES YOUR MONTH LOOK LIKE

Holidays:_____   Weekends:_____
Weekdays:_____   Other:_____

What **project(s)** do you plan on working on?

_____

What **goal** are you aiming to achieve?

_____

What will be your biggest **obstacle** this month?

_____

How will you **overcome** this? Or adjust for this?

_____

What will be your End of the Month **reward**?

_____

GOALS FOR THIS MONTH

Word Count:_____   Marketing Hours:_____
Brainstorming Hours:_____   Research Hours:_____
Editing Hours:_____   Reading Hours:_____

WEEK 1

DAILY ACCOMPLISHMENTS	**THURSDAY 1**
*Word Count:*_____	*Marketing Hours:*_____
*Brainstorming Hours:*_____	*Research Hours:*_____
*Editing Hours:*_____	*Reading Hours:*_____

DAILY ACCOMPLISHMENTS	**FRIDAY 2**
*Word Count:*_____	*Marketing Hours:*_____
*Brainstorming Hours:*_____	*Research Hours:*_____
*Editing Hours:*_____	*Reading Hours:*_____

DAILY ACCOMPLISHMENTS	**SATURDAY 3**
*Word Count:*_____	*Marketing Hours:*_____
*Brainstorming Hours:*_____	*Research Hours:*_____
*Editing Hours:*_____	*Reading Hours:*_____

DAILY ACCOMPLISHMENTS	**SUNDAY 4**
*Word Count:*_____	*Marketing Hours:*_____
*Brainstorming Hours:*_____	*Research Hours:*_____
*Editing Hours:*_____	*Reading Hours:*_____

DAILY ACCOMPLISHMENTS	**MONDAY 5**
*Word Count:*_____	*Marketing Hours:*_____
*Brainstorming Hours:*_____	*Research Hours:*_____
*Editing Hours:*_____	*Reading Hours:*_____

DAILY ACCOMPLISHMENTS	**TUESDAY 6**
*Word Count:*_____	*Marketing Hours:*_____
*Brainstorming Hours:*_____	*Research Hours:*_____
*Editing Hours:*_____	*Reading Hours:*_____

DAILY ACCOMPLISHMENTS	**WEDNESDAY 7**
*Word Count:*_____	*Marketing Hours:*_____
*Brainstorming Hours:*_____	*Research Hours:*_____
*Editing Hours:*_____	*Reading Hours:*_____

WEEKLY OVERVIEW

EXERCISE: Take 5-minute to write something with the 2 words below:

Run   Verge

Post your exercise on the 4HP Accountable Authors Group on Facebook!

What was your sprint time and top word count?

_____

List a new song you discovered this week:

_____

Favorite food or drink this week:

_____

How did you reward yourself?

_____

What project(s) did you work on?

_____

What are you reading?

_____

What went well this week?

_____

What could improve this week?

_____

_____

_____

TOTAL FOR THE WEEK

Word Count:_____   Marketing Hours:_____
Brainstorming Hours:_____   Research Hours:_____
Editing Hours:_____   Reading Hours:_____

Don't forget to color in your grid!

The Cheerleader
Who inspires you right now? Why?

THE ARCHITECT

Art time: Draw a map for your project.
It can be a town, a city, a galaxy, a
river system, an underground web
of tunnels, or a map to buried
treasure--whatever works for you!

THE RESEARCHER

"My inspiration comes from two words. The two most important words to a writer: What If?"

~ *Beth Revis*

THE TASKMASTER

How do you track your ideas? A journal's a great way to ensure you never lose a story idea.

Week 2

DAILY ACCOMPLISHMENTS	THURSDAY 8
Word Count: _____	Marketing Hours: _____
Brainstorming Hours: _____	Research Hours: _____
Editing Hours: _____	Reading Hours: _____

DAILY ACCOMPLISHMENTS	FRIDAY 9
Word Count: _____	Marketing Hours: _____
Brainstorming Hours: _____	Research Hours: _____
Editing Hours: _____	Reading Hours: _____

DAILY ACCOMPLISHMENTS	SATURDAY 10
Word Count: _____	Marketing Hours: _____
Brainstorming Hours: _____	Research Hours: _____
Editing Hours: _____	Reading Hours: _____

DAILY ACCOMPLISHMENTS	SUNDAY 11
Word Count: _____	Marketing Hours: _____
Brainstorming Hours: _____	Research Hours: _____
Editing Hours: _____	Reading Hours: _____

DAILY ACCOMPLISHMENTS	MONDAY 12
Word Count: _____	Marketing Hours: _____
Brainstorming Hours: _____	Research Hours: _____
Editing Hours: _____	Reading Hours: _____

DAILY ACCOMPLISHMENTS	TUESDAY 13
Word Count: _____	Marketing Hours: _____
Brainstorming Hours: _____	Research Hours: _____
Editing Hours: _____	Reading Hours: _____

DAILY ACCOMPLISHMENTS	WEDNESDAY 14
Word Count: _____	Marketing Hours: _____
Brainstorming Hours: _____	Research Hours: _____
Editing Hours: _____	Reading Hours: _____

WEEKLY OVERVIEW

EXERCISE: Take 5-minute to write something with the 2 words below:

Green   Speak

Post your exercise on the 4HP Accountable Authors Group on Facebook!

What was your sprint time and top word count?

_____

List a new song you discovered this week:

_____

Favorite food or drink this week:

_____

How did you reward yourself?

_____

What project(s) did you work on?

_____

What are you reading?

_____

What went well this week?

_____

What could improve this week?

_____

_____

_____

TOTAL FOR THE WEEK

Word Count:_____   Marketing Hours:_____
Brainstorming Hours:_____   Research Hours:_____
Editing Hours:_____   Reading Hours:_____

Don't forget to color in your grid!

APRIL

APRIL

The Cheerleader

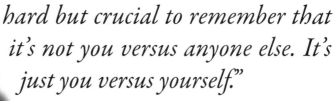

"There will always be someone ahead of you, and there will always be someone behind. It's hard but crucial to remember that it's not you versus anyone else. It's just you versus yourself."

~ V.E. Schwab

THE ARCHITECT

People watching is a great way to inspire stories.

THE RESEARCHER

What's your favorite book of all time? Why?

THE TASKMASTER

Spring Cleaning: Set a timer for seven minutes. Write down every project idea in your brain until the alarm rings. Get those thoughts on paper (*for later use on a future project*). Don't let them derail your current task.

APRIL

WEEK 3

DAILY ACCOMPLISHMENTS	THURSDAY 15
Word Count:	*Marketing Hours:*
Brainstorming Hours:	*Research Hours:*
Editing Hours:	*Reading Hours:*

DAILY ACCOMPLISHMENTS	FRIDAY 16
Word Count:	*Marketing Hours:*
Brainstorming Hours:	*Research Hours:*
Editing Hours:	*Reading Hours:*

DAILY ACCOMPLISHMENTS	SATURDAY 17
Word Count:	*Marketing Hours:*
Brainstorming Hours:	*Research Hours:*
Editing Hours:	*Reading Hours:*

DAILY ACCOMPLISHMENTS	SUNDAY 18
Word Count:	*Marketing Hours:*
Brainstorming Hours:	*Research Hours:*
Editing Hours:	*Reading Hours:*

DAILY ACCOMPLISHMENTS	MONDAY 19
Word Count:	*Marketing Hours:*
Brainstorming Hours:	*Research Hours:*
Editing Hours:	*Reading Hours:*

DAILY ACCOMPLISHMENTS	TUESDAY 20
Word Count:	*Marketing Hours:*
Brainstorming Hours:	*Research Hours:*
Editing Hours:	*Reading Hours:*

DAILY ACCOMPLISHMENTS	WEDNESDAY 21
Word Count:	*Marketing Hours:*
Brainstorming Hours:	*Research Hours:*
Editing Hours:	*Reading Hours:*

Weekly Overview

Carry   Watermelon

Post your exercise on the 4HP Accountable Authors Group on Facebook!

What was your sprint time and top word count?

_____

List a new song you discovered this week:

_____

Favorite food or drink this week:

_____

How did you reward yourself?

_____

What project(s) did you work on?

_____

What are you reading?

_____

What went well this week?

_____

What could improve this week?

_____

_____

_____

Total for the Week

Word Count:_____   Marketing Hours:_____
Brainstorming Hours:_____   Research Hours:_____
Editing Hours:_____   Reading Hours:_____

Don't forget to color in your grid!

APRIL

The Cheerleader

Record a moment when you last succeeded. You did that? You can totally do this.

THE ARCHITECT

Keep an eye out for "was." Rephrase the sentence to use more active verbs. Example:
She was walking across the street. Alternative: She walked across the street. She strode across the street. She strut her stuff across the pavement.

THE RESEARCHER

Trope Time: Research common tropes in your genre.
How are you following or breaking these models?

THE TASKMASTER

"A professional writer is an amateur who did not quit."
~ Richard Bach

You are a professional writer. How do I know this? You bought a skill book to keep you organized and on task. Only a professional would do that.

APRIL

DAILY ACCOMPLISHMENTS   **THURSDAY 22**

WORD COUNT:_____   MARKETING HOURS:_____
BRAINSTORMING HOURS:_____   RESEARCH HOURS:_____
EDITING HOURS:_____   READING HOURS:_____

DAILY ACCOMPLISHMENTS   **FRIDAY 23**

WORD COUNT:_____   MARKETING HOURS:_____
BRAINSTORMING HOURS:_____   RESEARCH HOURS:_____
EDITING HOURS:_____   READING HOURS:_____

DAILY ACCOMPLISHMENTS   **SATURDAY 24**

WORD COUNT:_____   MARKETING HOURS:_____
BRAINSTORMING HOURS:_____   RESEARCH HOURS:_____
EDITING HOURS:_____   READING HOURS:_____

DAILY ACCOMPLISHMENTS   **SUNDAY 25**

WORD COUNT:_____   MARKETING HOURS:_____
BRAINSTORMING HOURS:_____   RESEARCH HOURS:_____
EDITING HOURS:_____   READING HOURS:_____

DAILY ACCOMPLISHMENTS   **MONDAY 26**

WORD COUNT:_____   MARKETING HOURS:_____
BRAINSTORMING HOURS:_____   RESEARCH HOURS:_____
EDITING HOURS:_____   READING HOURS:_____

DAILY ACCOMPLISHMENTS   **TUESDAY 27**

WORD COUNT:_____   MARKETING HOURS:_____
BRAINSTORMING HOURS:_____   RESEARCH HOURS:_____
EDITING HOURS:_____   READING HOURS:_____

DAILY ACCOMPLISHMENTS   **WEDNESDAY 28**

WORD COUNT:_____   MARKETING HOURS:_____
BRAINSTORMING HOURS:_____   RESEARCH HOURS:_____
EDITING HOURS:_____   READING HOURS:_____

APRIL

WEEKLY OVERVIEW

EXERCISE: Take 5-minute to write something with the 2 words below:

Tickle   Straw

Post your exercise on the 4HP Accountable Authors Group on Facebook!

What was your sprint time and top word count?

_____

List a new song you discovered this week:

_____

Favorite food or drink this week:

_____

How did you reward yourself?

_____

What project(s) did you work on?

_____

What are you reading?

_____

What went well this week?

_____

What could improve this week?

_____

_____

_____

TOTAL FOR THE WEEK

Word Count:_____   Marketing Hours:_____
Brainstorming Hours:_____   Research Hours:_____
Editing Hours:_____   Reading Hours:_____

Don't forget to color in your grid!

The Cheerleader

"You've got to jump off cliffs and build your wings on the way down."

~ Ray Bradbury

THE ARCHITECT

Keep it Active: Add a phrase after your sentence such as "by bunnies." (*The car was driven into the field by bunnies.*) If it makes sense, the sentence is passive. Consider revising to be more active. (*The bunnies drove the car into the field.*) When bunnies (*or kitties or zombies*) don't make sense, you've got it!

THE RESEARCHER

Doing sprints for 10, 20, or 30 minutes at a time will keep your writing at a good pace. Between chores perhaps?
What's your average word count? Research your productivity!

THE TASKMASTER

You have fans (*or will have fans if you haven't been published yet*). Even if you can't see them, they're rooting for you--so don't forget to root for yourself!

DAILY ACCOMPLISHMENTS	THURSDAY 29
WORD COUNT:_____	MARKETING HOURS:_____
BRAINSTORMING HOURS:_____	RESEARCH HOURS:_____
EDITING HOURS:_____	READING HOURS:_____

DAILY ACCOMPLISHMENTS	FRIDAY 30
WORD COUNT:_____	MARKETING HOURS:_____
BRAINSTORMING HOURS:_____	RESEARCH HOURS:_____
EDITING HOURS:_____	READING HOURS:_____

THE ARCHITECT

Find a podcast about authors, writing, even book reviews on books similar to your own. Get to know your fellow authors! (*We recommend Drinking with Authors*).

Listen to it as you go outside for a walk. Exercise is important. Self-care has to be part of your day-to-day routine. Learning more about writing is important too!

APRIL

Weekly Overview

EXERCISE: Take 5-minute to write something with the 2 words below:

Summon   Delirious

Post your exercise on the 4HP Accountable Authors Group on Facebook!

What was your sprint time and top word count?

_____

List a new song you discovered this week:

_____

Favorite food or drink this week:

_____

How did you reward yourself?

_____

What project(s) did you work on?

_____

What are you reading?

_____

What went well this week?

_____

What could improve this week?

_____

_____

_____

TOTAL FOR THE WEEK

Word Count:_____   Marketing Hours:_____
Brainstorming Hours:_____   Research Hours:_____
Editing Hours:_____   Reading Hours:_____

Don't forget to color in your grid!

MONTHLY ACTIVITY GRID

APRIL

WRITING OR WORD COUNT	1 2 3 4 5 6 7 8 9 10 11 12 13 14 15 16 17 18 19 20 21 22 23 24 25 26 27 28 29 30 31
BRAINSTORMING	
EDITING	
MARKETING OR SOCIAL MEDIA	
RESEARCH	
READING	
OTHER:	

YOUR AVERAGE WORD COUNT FOR THE MONTH

Total Word Count:_____ Divided by _____ days =_____

TOTAL FOR THE YEAR SO FAR

Word Count:_____   Marketing Hours:_____
Brainstorming Hours:_____   Research Hours:_____
Editing Hours:_____   Reading Hours:_____

JOURNAL

APRIL

What was your **top week**?

_____

What made your **top week** successful?

_____

What was your biggest **obstacle**?

_____

How did you **overcome** this? Or could do better next time?

_____

_____

What was your biggest **achievement**?

_____

_____

What **inspired** you most this month?

_____

Did you **discover** a new writing tip or advice this month?

_____

_____

TOTAL FOR THE MONTH

Word Count:_____   Research Hours:_____
Brainstorming Hours:_____   Reading Hours:_____
Editing Hours:_____
Marketing Hours:_____

TOTAL FOR THE YEAR SO FAR

Word Count:_____   Research Hours:_____
Brainstorming Hours:_____   Reading Hours:_____
Editing Hours:_____
Marketing Hours:_____

Don't forget to color in your grid!

MAY

The school year may almost be over. You might have to attend a graduation or be graduating yourself. Do not let that slow you down. Maybe grab your laptop, go write outside, and enjoy all that nature around you inspires.

May 31 - Memorial Day

WHAT DOES YOUR MONTH LOOK LIKE

Holidays:_____   Weekends:_____
Weekdays:_____   Other:_____

What **project(s)** do you plan on working on?

_____

What **goal** are you aiming to achieve?

_____

What will be your biggest **obstacle** this month?

_____

How will you **overcome** this? Or adjust for this?

_____

What will be your End of the Month **reward**?

_____

GOALS FOR THIS MONTH

Word Count:_____   Marketing Hours:_____
Brainstorming Hours:_____   Research Hours:_____
Editing Hours:_____   Reading Hours:_____

WEEK 1

DAILY ACCOMPLISHMENTS   **SATURDAY 1**

WORD COUNT:_____   MARKETING HOURS:_____
BRAINSTORMING HOURS:_____   RESEARCH HOURS:_____
EDITING HOURS:_____   READING HOURS:_____

DAILY ACCOMPLISHMENTS   **SUNDAY 2**

WORD COUNT:_____   MARKETING HOURS:_____
BRAINSTORMING HOURS:_____   RESEARCH HOURS:_____
EDITING HOURS:_____   READING HOURS:_____

DAILY ACCOMPLISHMENTS   **MONDAY 3**

WORD COUNT:_____   MARKETING HOURS:_____
BRAINSTORMING HOURS:_____   RESEARCH HOURS:_____
EDITING HOURS:_____   READING HOURS:_____

DAILY ACCOMPLISHMENTS   **TUESDAY 4**

WORD COUNT:_____   MARKETING HOURS:_____
BRAINSTORMING HOURS:_____   RESEARCH HOURS:_____
EDITING HOURS:_____   READING HOURS:_____

DAILY ACCOMPLISHMENTS   **WEDNESDAY 5**

WORD COUNT:_____   MARKETING HOURS:_____
BRAINSTORMING HOURS:_____   RESEARCH HOURS:_____
EDITING HOURS:_____   READING HOURS:_____

DAILY ACCOMPLISHMENTS   **THURSDAY 6**

WORD COUNT:_____   MARKETING HOURS:_____
BRAINSTORMING HOURS:_____   RESEARCH HOURS:_____
EDITING HOURS:_____   READING HOURS:_____

DAILY ACCOMPLISHMENTS   **FRIDAY 7**

WORD COUNT:_____   MARKETING HOURS:_____
BRAINSTORMING HOURS:_____   RESEARCH HOURS:_____
EDITING HOURS:_____   READING HOURS:_____

WEEKLY OVERVIEW

EXERCISE: Take 5-minute to write something with the 2 words below:

Horse   Lotion

Post your exercise on the 4HP Accountable Authors Group on Facebook!

What was your sprint time and top word count?

_____

List a new song you discovered this week:

_____

Favorite food or drink this week:

_____

How did you reward yourself?

_____

What project(s) did you work on?

_____

What are you reading?

_____

What went well this week?

_____

What could improve this week?

_____

_____

_____

TOTAL FOR THE WEEK

Word Count:_____ Marketing Hours:_____
Brainstorming Hours:_____ Research Hours:_____
Editing Hours:_____ Reading Hours:_____

Don't forget to color in your grid!

MAY

The Cheerleader

"I don't give a damn what other people think. It's entirely their own business. I'm not writing for other people."
~ Harold Pinter

THE ARCHITECT

Big Picture Time: Step back and craft a visual of your project. This could be a timeline of events, a layout of connections between characters, a world overview, or anything related to the entire package.

THE RESEARCHER

Research real religions, climates, maps, and political structures to help inspire your worldbuilding.
This is especially important if you're writing fantasy but can still be incorporated in contemporary works.

THE TASKMASTER

Increase your word count for next week regardless of your target. Little jumps help get you there faster.

DAILY ACCOMPLISHMENTS	**SATURDAY 8**
WORD COUNT:	*MARKETING HOURS:*
BRAINSTORMING HOURS:	*RESEARCH HOURS:*
EDITING HOURS:	*READING HOURS:*

DAILY ACCOMPLISHMENTS	**SUNDAY 9**
WORD COUNT:	*MARKETING HOURS:*
BRAINSTORMING HOURS:	*RESEARCH HOURS:*
EDITING HOURS:	*READING HOURS:*

DAILY ACCOMPLISHMENTS	**MONDAY 10**
WORD COUNT:	*MARKETING HOURS:*
BRAINSTORMING HOURS:	*RESEARCH HOURS:*
EDITING HOURS:	*READING HOURS:*

DAILY ACCOMPLISHMENTS	**TUESDAY 11**
WORD COUNT:	*MARKETING HOURS:*
BRAINSTORMING HOURS:	*RESEARCH HOURS:*
EDITING HOURS:	*READING HOURS:*

DAILY ACCOMPLISHMENTS	**WEDNESDAY 12**
WORD COUNT:	*MARKETING HOURS:*
BRAINSTORMING HOURS:	*RESEARCH HOURS:*
EDITING HOURS:	*READING HOURS:*

DAILY ACCOMPLISHMENTS	**THURSDAY 13**
WORD COUNT:	*MARKETING HOURS:*
BRAINSTORMING HOURS:	*RESEARCH HOURS:*
EDITING HOURS:	*READING HOURS:*

DAILY ACCOMPLISHMENTS	**FRIDAY 14**
WORD COUNT:	*MARKETING HOURS:*
BRAINSTORMING HOURS:	*RESEARCH HOURS:*
EDITING HOURS:	*READING HOURS:*

MAY

EXERCISE: Take 5-minute to write something with the 2 words below:

Mint   Clock

Post your exercise on the 4HP Accountable Authors Group on Facebook!

What was your sprint time and top word count?

_____

List a new song you discovered this week:

_____

Favorite food or drink this week:

_____

How did you reward yourself?

_____

What project(s) did you work on?

_____

What are you reading?

_____

What went well this week?

_____

What could improve this week?

_____

_____

_____

TOTAL FOR THE WEEK

Word Count:_____   Marketing Hours:_____
Brainstorming Hours:_____   Research Hours:_____
Editing Hours:_____   Reading Hours:_____

Don't forget to color in your grid!

The Cheerleader

Focus on editing your work once this week. How's it coming along?

THE ARCHITECT

"If I waited for perfection, I would never write a word."

~ Margaret Atwood

THE RESEARCHER

Time to Ctrl+F those words you overuse. List the troublesome words that keep sneaking back in.

THE TASKMASTER

Are you overediting your work? Stop it. Get the entire story on paper first. Then go back and review what you've done. It's easy to fall into the editing trap during drafting when you have to circle back.

MAY

Week 3

DAILY ACCOMPLISHMENTS	SATURDAY 15
Word Count:	Marketing Hours:
Brainstorming Hours:	Research Hours:
Editing Hours:	Reading Hours:

DAILY ACCOMPLISHMENTS	SUNDAY 16
Word Count:	Marketing Hours:
Brainstorming Hours:	Research Hours:
Editing Hours:	Reading Hours:

DAILY ACCOMPLISHMENTS	MONDAY 17
Word Count:	Marketing Hours:
Brainstorming Hours:	Research Hours:
Editing Hours:	Reading Hours:

DAILY ACCOMPLISHMENTS	TUESDAY 18
Word Count:	Marketing Hours:
Brainstorming Hours:	Research Hours:
Editing Hours:	Reading Hours:

DAILY ACCOMPLISHMENTS	WEDNESDAY 19
Word Count:	Marketing Hours:
Brainstorming Hours:	Research Hours:
Editing Hours:	Reading Hours:

DAILY ACCOMPLISHMENTS	THURSDAY 20
Word Count:	Marketing Hours:
Brainstorming Hours:	Research Hours:
Editing Hours:	Reading Hours:

DAILY ACCOMPLISHMENTS	FRIDAY 21
Word Count:	Marketing Hours:
Brainstorming Hours:	Research Hours:
Editing Hours:	Reading Hours:

Weekly Overview

EXERCISE: Take 5-minute to write something with the 2 words below:

Octopus   Hard Drive

Post your exercise on the 4HP Accountable Authors Group on Facebook!

What was your sprint time and top word count?

_____

List a new song you discovered this week:

_____

Favorite food or drink this week:

_____

How did you reward yourself?

_____

What project(s) did you work on?

_____

What are you reading?

_____

What went well this week?

_____

What could improve this week?

_____

_____

_____

Total for the Week

Word Count:_____   Marketing Hours:_____

Brainstorming Hours:_____   Research Hours:_____

Editing Hours:_____   Reading Hours:_____

Don't forget to color in your grid!

MAY

The Cheerleader

A spoonful of sugar helps the medicine go down. Record one sweet thing that offsets one negative thing this week!

THE ARCHITECT

Blurb Time: Revisit the blurb for the current project.
Does this still work?
Jot down ideas for tweaks here.

THE RESEARCHER

"Only those who will risk going too far can possibly find out how far one can go."

~ T.S. Eliot

THE TASKMASTER

Are you stuck?
Go talk to someone, anyone, about your story. Even if they say nothing useful, talking it out will help you move forward.

MAY

DAILY ACCOMPLISHMENTS   **SATURDAY 22**

Word Count:_____ Marketing Hours:_____
Brainstorming Hours:_____ Research Hours:_____
Editing Hours:_____ Reading Hours:_____

DAILY ACCOMPLISHMENTS   **SUNDAY 23**

Word Count:_____ Marketing Hours:_____
Brainstorming Hours:_____ Research Hours:_____
Editing Hours:_____ Reading Hours:_____

DAILY ACCOMPLISHMENTS   **MONDAY 24**

Word Count:_____ Marketing Hours:_____
Brainstorming Hours:_____ Research Hours:_____
Editing Hours:_____ Reading Hours:_____

DAILY ACCOMPLISHMENTS   **TUESDAY 25**

Word Count:_____ Marketing Hours:_____
Brainstorming Hours:_____ Research Hours:_____
Editing Hours:_____ Reading Hours:_____

DAILY ACCOMPLISHMENTS   **WEDNESDAY 26**

Word Count:_____ Marketing Hours:_____
Brainstorming Hours:_____ Research Hours:_____
Editing Hours:_____ Reading Hours:_____

DAILY ACCOMPLISHMENTS   **THURSDAY 27**

Word Count:_____ Marketing Hours:_____
Brainstorming Hours:_____ Research Hours:_____
Editing Hours:_____ Reading Hours:_____

DAILY ACCOMPLISHMENTS   **FRIDAY 28**

Word Count:_____ Marketing Hours:_____
Brainstorming Hours:_____ Research Hours:_____
Editing Hours:_____ Reading Hours:_____

MAY

Weekly Overview

EXERCISE: Take 5-minute to write something with the 2 words below:

Moon   Shirt

Post your exercise on the 4HP Accountable Authors Group on Facebook!

What was your sprint time and top word count?

_____

List a new song you discovered this week:

_____

Favorite food or drink this week:

_____

How did you reward yourself?

_____

What project(s) did you work on?

_____

What are you reading?

_____

What went well this week?

_____

What could improve this week?

_____

_____

_____

TOTAL FOR THE WEEK

Word Count:_____   Marketing Hours:_____
Brainstorming Hours:_____   Research Hours:_____
Editing Hours:_____   Reading Hours:_____

Don't forget to color in your grid!

The Cheerleader

"We are never ready. The only chance we have to reach our true potential is when we rise to the challenges that life throws at us."

~ Merlin and Arthur

THE ARCHITECT

Coffee vs. Tea
vs Wine.
Discuss.

THE RESEARCHER

What is your favorite way to write? Sometimes listening to music from the time or place you're writing about will get you into your character's headspace quicker. Give it a try!

THE TASKMASTER

Life will happen to you. Acknowledge it, understand it, then move on. Don't let it stop your creativity. Let it fuel you to create more.

MAY

DAILY ACCOMPLISHMENTS	**SATURDAY 29**
WORD COUNT:	MARKETING HOURS:
BRAINSTORMING HOURS:	RESEARCH HOURS:
EDITING HOURS:	READING HOURS:

DAILY ACCOMPLISHMENTS	**SUNDAY 30**
WORD COUNT:	MARKETING HOURS:
BRAINSTORMING HOURS:	RESEARCH HOURS:
EDITING HOURS:	READING HOURS:

DAILY ACCOMPLISHMENTS	**MONDAY 31**
WORD COUNT:	MARKETING HOURS:
BRAINSTORMING HOURS:	RESEARCH HOURS:
EDITING HOURS:	READING HOURS:

MAY

THE TASKMASTER

Now is the time to establish your luck for this month. If you do not see a rainbow, create it. You decide on your version of the pot of gold, but be sure to set your goals so that you can succeed. Don't forget that you can join the 4HP Accountable Authors group on Facebook and find people just like you to collaborate with. Good luck, Fellow Author!

Weekly Overview

Exercise: Take 5-minute to write something with the 2 words below:

Holistic   Jaundice

Post your exercise on the 4HP Accountable Authors Group on Facebook!

What was your sprint time and top word count?

_____

List a new song you discovered this week:

_____

Favorite food or drink this week:

_____

How did you reward yourself?

_____

What project(s) did you work on?

_____

What are you reading?

_____

What went well this week?

_____

What could improve this week?

_____

_____

_____

Total for the Week

Word Count:_____   Marketing Hours:_____
Brainstorming Hours:_____   Research Hours:_____
Editing Hours:_____   Reading Hours:_____

Don't forget to color in your grid!

MAY

MONTHLY ACTIVITY GRID

MAY

WRITING OR WORD COUNT	
BRAINSTORMING	
EDITING	
MARKETING OR SOCIAL MEDIA	
RESEARCH	
READING	
OTHER:	

1 2 3 4 5 6 7 8 9 10 11 12 13 14 15 16 17 18 19 20 21 22 23 24 25 26 27 28 29 30 31

YOUR AVERAGE WORD COUNT FOR THE MONTH

Total Word Count:_____ Divided by _____ days =_____

TOTAL FOR THE YEAR SO FAR

Word Count:_____ Marketing Hours:_____
Brainstorming Hours:_____ Research Hours:_____
Editing Hours:_____ Reading Hours:_____

JOURNAL

MAY

What was your **top week**?

_____

What made your **top week** successful?

_____

What was your biggest **obstacle**?

_____

How did you **overcome** this? Or could do better next time?

_____

_____

What was your biggest **achievement**?

_____

_____

What **inspired** you most this month?

_____

Did you **discover** a new writing tip or advice this month?

_____

_____

TOTAL FOR THE MONTH

Word Count:_____   Research Hours:_____
Brainstorming Hours:_____   Reading Hours:_____
Editing Hours:_____
Marketing Hours:_____

TOTAL FOR THE YEAR SO FAR

Word Count:_____   Research Hours:_____
Brainstorming Hours:_____   Reading Hours:_____
Editing Hours:_____
Marketing Hours:_____

Don't forget to color in your grid!

JUNE

Y ou're moving into the halfway mark for the year. Take this time to truly evaluate what is working and not. If you need to change something and you have been putting it off, do it now! You still have time to meet or exceed your goals for this year. We believe in you!

School is Out!
Summer Vacations!

WHAT DOES YOUR MONTH LOOK LIKE

Holidays:_____   Weekends:_____
Weekdays:_____   Other:_____

What **project(s)** do you plan on working on?

_____

What **goal** are you aiming to achieve?

_____

What will be your biggest **obstacle** this month?

_____

How will you **overcome** this? Or adjust for this?

_____

What will be your End of the Month **reward**?

_____

GOALS FOR THIS MONTH

Word Count:_____   Marketing Hours:_____
Brainstorming Hours:_____   Research Hours:_____
Editing Hours:_____   Reading Hours:_____

Week 1

DAILY ACCOMPLISHMENTS   **TUESDAY 1**

WORD COUNT:_____   MARKETING HOURS:_____

BRAINSTORMING HOURS:_____   RESEARCH HOURS:_____

EDITING HOURS:_____   READING HOURS:_____

DAILY ACCOMPLISHMENTS   **WEDNESDAY 2**

WORD COUNT:_____   MARKETING HOURS:_____

BRAINSTORMING HOURS:_____   RESEARCH HOURS:_____

EDITING HOURS:_____   READING HOURS:_____

DAILY ACCOMPLISHMENTS   **THURSDAY 3**

WORD COUNT:_____   MARKETING HOURS:_____

BRAINSTORMING HOURS:_____   RESEARCH HOURS:_____

EDITING HOURS:_____   READING HOURS:_____

DAILY ACCOMPLISHMENTS   **FRIDAY 4**

WORD COUNT:_____   MARKETING HOURS:_____

BRAINSTORMING HOURS:_____   RESEARCH HOURS:_____

EDITING HOURS:_____   READING HOURS:_____

DAILY ACCOMPLISHMENTS   **SATURDAY 5**

WORD COUNT:_____   MARKETING HOURS:_____

BRAINSTORMING HOURS:_____   RESEARCH HOURS:_____

EDITING HOURS:_____   READING HOURS:_____

DAILY ACCOMPLISHMENTS   **SUNDAY 6**

WORD COUNT:_____   MARKETING HOURS:_____

BRAINSTORMING HOURS:_____   RESEARCH HOURS:_____

EDITING HOURS:_____   READING HOURS:_____

DAILY ACCOMPLISHMENTS   **MONDAY 7**

WORD COUNT:_____   MARKETING HOURS:_____

BRAINSTORMING HOURS:_____   RESEARCH HOURS:_____

EDITING HOURS:_____   READING HOURS:_____

WEEKLY OVERVIEW

EXERCISE: Take 5-minute to write something with the 2 words below:

Sticker   Cat

Post your exercise on the 4HP Accountable Authors Group on Facebook!

What was your sprint time and top word count?

_____

List a new song you discovered this week:

_____

Favorite food or drink this week:

_____

How did you reward yourself?

_____

What project(s) did you work on?

_____

What are you reading?

_____

What went well this week?

_____

What could improve this week?

_____

_____

_____

TOTAL FOR THE WEEK

Word Count:_____   Marketing Hours:_____
Brainstorming Hours:_____   Research Hours:_____
Editing Hours:_____   Reading Hours:_____

Don't forget to color in your grid!

The Cheerleader

Find something that "Sparks Joy" and keep it within sight of your writing space. Sometimes you need a gentle reminder to stay positive.

THE ARCHITECT

Weave subtext througout your writing. This will give your story a layered, nuanced message that isn't shoved into the reader's face.

THE RESEARCHER

"The difference between the right word and the almost right word is the difference between a lightning bug and the lightning."

~ Mark Twain

THE TASKMASTER

Find out if your favorite author has advice on writing. Does it inspire you? It should. There's a reason they're your favorite.

WEEK 2

DAILY ACCOMPLISHMENTS	**TUESDAY 8**
WORD COUNT:	MARKETING HOURS:
BRAINSTORMING HOURS:	RESEARCH HOURS:
EDITING HOURS:	READING HOURS:

DAILY ACCOMPLISHMENTS	**WEDNESDAY 9**
WORD COUNT:	MARKETING HOURS:
BRAINSTORMING HOURS:	RESEARCH HOURS:
EDITING HOURS:	READING HOURS:

DAILY ACCOMPLISHMENTS	**THURSDAY 10**
WORD COUNT:	MARKETING HOURS:
BRAINSTORMING HOURS:	RESEARCH HOURS:
EDITING HOURS:	READING HOURS:

DAILY ACCOMPLISHMENTS	**FRIDAY 11**
WORD COUNT:	MARKETING HOURS:
BRAINSTORMING HOURS:	RESEARCH HOURS:
EDITING HOURS:	READING HOURS:

DAILY ACCOMPLISHMENTS	**SATURDAY 12**
WORD COUNT:	MARKETING HOURS:
BRAINSTORMING HOURS:	RESEARCH HOURS:
EDITING HOURS:	READING HOURS:

DAILY ACCOMPLISHMENTS	**SUNDAY 13**
WORD COUNT:	MARKETING HOURS:
BRAINSTORMING HOURS:	RESEARCH HOURS:
EDITING HOURS:	READING HOURS:

DAILY ACCOMPLISHMENTS	**MONDAY 14**
WORD COUNT:	MARKETING HOURS:
BRAINSTORMING HOURS:	RESEARCH HOURS:
EDITING HOURS:	READING HOURS:

WEEKLY OVERVIEW

EXERCISE: Take 5-minute to write something with the 2 words below:

Lawn   Ice

Post your exercise on the 4HP Accountable Authors Group on Facebook!

What was your sprint time and top word count?

_____

List a new song you discovered this week:

_____

Favorite food or drink this week:

_____

How did you reward yourself?

_____

What project(s) did you work on?

_____

What are you reading?

_____

What went well this week?

_____

What could improve this week?

_____

_____

_____

TOTAL FOR THE WEEK

Word Count:_____   Marketing Hours:_____
Brainstorming Hours:_____   Research Hours:_____
Editing Hours:_____   Reading Hours:_____

Don't forget to color in your grid!

The Cheerleader

Art Time: Sketch yourself reaching your year end writing goals. Visualization helps with motivation!

THE ARCHITECT

"You don't understand an antagonist until you understand why he's a protagonist in his own version of the world."

~ John Rogers

THE RESEARCHER

Five Minute Break Time:
Stand up. Walk around. Go outside
if you can. Look skyward, study a
different wall, check out a new
space. Set a timer, then return to
writing when it goes off.

THE TASKMASTER

Stop wondering if you're
good enough. You are. In
fact, you are great. So get
over it and keep writing.

WEEK 3

DAILY ACCOMPLISHMENTS	**TUESDAY 15**
Word Count:_____	Marketing Hours:_____
Brainstorming Hours:_____	Research Hours:_____
Editing Hours:_____	Reading Hours:_____

DAILY ACCOMPLISHMENTS	**WEDNESDAY 16**
Word Count:_____	Marketing Hours:_____
Brainstorming Hours:_____	Research Hours:_____
Editing Hours:_____	Reading Hours:_____

DAILY ACCOMPLISHMENTS	**THURSDAY 17**
Word Count:_____	Marketing Hours:_____
Brainstorming Hours:_____	Research Hours:_____
Editing Hours:_____	Reading Hours:_____

DAILY ACCOMPLISHMENTS	**FRIDAY 18**
Word Count:_____	Marketing Hours:_____
Brainstorming Hours:_____	Research Hours:_____
Editing Hours:_____	Reading Hours:_____

DAILY ACCOMPLISHMENTS	**SATURDAY 19**
Word Count:_____	Marketing Hours:_____
Brainstorming Hours:_____	Research Hours:_____
Editing Hours:_____	Reading Hours:_____

DAILY ACCOMPLISHMENTS	**SUNDAY 20**
Word Count:_____	Marketing Hours:_____
Brainstorming Hours:_____	Research Hours:_____
Editing Hours:_____	Reading Hours:_____

DAILY ACCOMPLISHMENTS	**MONDAY 21**
Word Count:_____	Marketing Hours:_____
Brainstorming Hours:_____	Research Hours:_____
Editing Hours:_____	Reading Hours:_____

JUNE

Weekly Overview

Tree   Photo

What was your sprint time and top word count?

_____

List a new song you discovered this week:

_____

Favorite food or drink this week:

_____

How did you reward yourself?

_____

What project(s) did you work on?

_____

What are you reading?

_____

What went well this week?

_____

What could improve this week?

_____

_____

_____

Total for the Week

Word Count:_____   Marketing Hours:_____
Brainstorming Hours:_____   Research Hours:_____
Editing Hours:_____   Reading Hours:_____

Don't forget to color in your grid!

JUNE

The Cheerleader

"Every single day the quality of my writing is improving."

~ Bryn Donovan

THE ARCHITECT

The original or the remake-- which is better? Defend your position.

THE RESEARCHER

Sensory Overload: Describe your surroundings by using all five senses.

THE TASKMASTER

No, it won't be perfect. Nothing is "perfect," so don't wait for that. Instead, keep improving by producing more work. That is the only way.

JUNE

WEEK 4

DAILY ACCOMPLISHMENTS	TUESDAY 22
WORD COUNT:	MARKETING HOURS:
BRAINSTORMING HOURS:	RESEARCH HOURS:
EDITING HOURS:	READING HOURS:

DAILY ACCOMPLISHMENTS	WEDNESDAY 23
WORD COUNT:	MARKETING HOURS:
BRAINSTORMING HOURS:	RESEARCH HOURS:
EDITING HOURS:	READING HOURS:

DAILY ACCOMPLISHMENTS	THURSDAY 24
WORD COUNT:	MARKETING HOURS:
BRAINSTORMING HOURS:	RESEARCH HOURS:
EDITING HOURS:	READING HOURS:

DAILY ACCOMPLISHMENTS	FRIDAY 25
WORD COUNT:	MARKETING HOURS:
BRAINSTORMING HOURS:	RESEARCH HOURS:
EDITING HOURS:	READING HOURS:

DAILY ACCOMPLISHMENTS	SATURDAY 26
WORD COUNT:	MARKETING HOURS:
BRAINSTORMING HOURS:	RESEARCH HOURS:
EDITING HOURS:	READING HOURS:

DAILY ACCOMPLISHMENTS	SUNDAY 27
WORD COUNT:	MARKETING HOURS:
BRAINSTORMING HOURS:	RESEARCH HOURS:
EDITING HOURS:	READING HOURS:

DAILY ACCOMPLISHMENTS	MONDAY 28
WORD COUNT:	MARKETING HOURS:
BRAINSTORMING HOURS:	RESEARCH HOURS:
EDITING HOURS:	READING HOURS:

Weekly Overview

Exercise: Take 5-minute to write something with the 2 words below:

Melt   Thumb

Post your exercise on the 4HP Accountable Authors Group on Facebook!

What was your sprint time and top word count?

_____

List a new song you discovered this week:

_____

Favorite food or drink this week:

_____

How did you reward yourself?

_____

What project(s) did you work on?

_____

What are you reading?

_____

What went well this week?

_____

What could improve this week?

_____

_____

_____

Total for the Week

Word Count:_____   Marketing Hours:_____
Brainstorming Hours:_____   Research Hours:_____
Editing Hours:_____   Reading Hours:_____

Don't forget to color in your grid!

The Cheerleader

Post the blurb of your current project on the 4HP Accountable Authors group on Facebook.

THE ARCHITECT

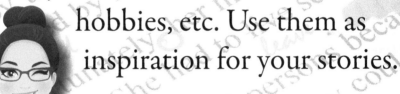

Pay attention to the things that excite you: music, books, movies, hobbies, etc. Use them as inspiration for your stories.

THE RESEARCHER

When was the last time you visited a library? Do you have a library card? If you haven't been in a while, go check it out. Get into the habit of visiting once a month.

THE TASKMASTER

"The world is a mess, and I just need to rule it."
~ Dr. Horrible (Dr. Horrible's Sing-a-Long Blog)

It is a mess, and your writing will inspire or provide an escape for your readers. So get a move on, use your hammer, and get it done.

DAILY ACCOMPLISHMENTS	**TUESDAY 29**
*WORD COUNT:*_____	*MARKETING HOURS:*_____
*BRAINSTORMING HOURS:*_____	*RESEARCH HOURS:*_____
*EDITING HOURS:*_____	*READING HOURS:*_____

DAILY ACCOMPLISHMENTS	**WEDNESDAY 30**
*WORD COUNT:*_____	*MARKETING HOURS:*_____
*BRAINSTORMING HOURS:*_____	*RESEARCH HOURS:*_____
*EDITING HOURS:*_____	*READING HOURS:*_____

The Cheerleader

Stuff You Should Know: You're halfway there! If you were flying to the moon, you'd have traveled 180,000 km by now (*assuming the moon is at its closest point to the earth.*) June 30th is the 181st day of the year (*if it's not a leap year*), so that means you would've traveled 994.5 km each day to get where you are right now. That's nearly 619 miles so far--and the Proclaimers only made it 500! Keep going!

JUNE

WEEKLY OVERVIEW

EXERCISE: Take 5-minute to write something with the 2 words below:

Rustic   Operate

Post your exercise on the 4HP Accountable Authors Group on Facebook!

What was your sprint time and top word count?

_____

List a new song you discovered this week:

_____

Favorite food or drink this week:

_____

How did you reward yourself?

_____

What project(s) did you work on?

_____

What are you reading?

_____

What went well this week?

_____

What could improve this week?

_____

_____

_____

TOTAL FOR THE WEEK

Word Count:_____ Marketing Hours:_____
Brainstorming Hours:_____ Research Hours:_____
Editing Hours:_____ Reading Hours:_____

Don't forget to color in your grid!

MONTHLY ACTIVITY GRID

WRITING OR WORD COUNT	
BRAINSTORMING	
EDITING	
MARKETING OR SOCIAL MEDIA	
RESEARCH	
READING	
OTHER:	

JUNE

YOUR AVERAGE WORD COUNT FOR THE MONTH

Total Word Count:_____ Divided by _____ days =_____

TOTAL FOR THE YEAR SO FAR

Word Count:_____   Marketing Hours:_____
Brainstorming Hours:_____   Research Hours:_____
Editing Hours:_____   Reading Hours:_____

JOURNAL

What was your **top week**?

_____

What made your **top week** successful?

_____

What was your biggest **obstacle**?

_____

How did you **overcome** this? Or could do better next time?

_____

_____

What was your biggest **achievement**?

_____

_____

What **inspired** you most this month?

_____

Did you **discover** a new writing tip or advice this month?

_____

_____

JUNE

TOTAL FOR THE MONTH

Word Count:_____   Research Hours:_____
Brainstorming Hours:_____   Reading Hours:_____
Editing Hours:_____
Marketing Hours:_____

TOTAL FOR THE YEAR SO FAR

Word Count:_____   Research Hours:_____
Brainstorming Hours:_____   Reading Hours:_____
Editing Hours:_____
Marketing Hours:_____

Don't forget to color in your grid!

JULY

This can be one of the most distracting times of year with fun in the sun. You can always go outside and write. Maybe even find a local coffee shop where the atmosphere is perfect to feel inspired and people watch at the same time.

Jul 4th - Independence Day

WHAT DOES YOUR MONTH LOOK LIKE

Holidays:_____   Weekends:_____
Weekdays:_____   Other:_____

What **project(s)** do you plan on working on?

_____

What **goal** are you aiming to achieve?

_____

What will be your biggest **obstacle** this month?

_____

How will you **overcome** this? Or adjust for this?

_____

What will be your End of the Month **reward**?

_____

GOALS FOR THIS MONTH

Word Count:_____   Marketing Hours:_____
Brainstorming Hours:_____   Research Hours:_____
Editing Hours:_____   Reading Hours:_____

JULY

WEEK 1

DAILY ACCOMPLISHMENTS	**THURSDAY 1**
WORD COUNT:_____	MARKETING HOURS:_____
BRAINSTORMING HOURS:_____	RESEARCH HOURS:_____
EDITING HOURS:_____	READING HOURS:_____

DAILY ACCOMPLISHMENTS	**FRIDAY 2**
WORD COUNT:_____	MARKETING HOURS:_____
BRAINSTORMING HOURS:_____	RESEARCH HOURS:_____
EDITING HOURS:_____	READING HOURS:_____

DAILY ACCOMPLISHMENTS	**SATURDAY 3**
WORD COUNT:_____	MARKETING HOURS:_____
BRAINSTORMING HOURS:_____	RESEARCH HOURS:_____
EDITING HOURS:_____	READING HOURS:_____

DAILY ACCOMPLISHMENTS	**SUNDAY 4**
WORD COUNT:_____	MARKETING HOURS:_____
BRAINSTORMING HOURS:_____	RESEARCH HOURS:_____
EDITING HOURS:_____	READING HOURS:_____

DAILY ACCOMPLISHMENTS	**MONDAY 5**
WORD COUNT:_____	MARKETING HOURS:_____
BRAINSTORMING HOURS:_____	RESEARCH HOURS:_____
EDITING HOURS:_____	READING HOURS:_____

DAILY ACCOMPLISHMENTS	**TUESDAY 6**
WORD COUNT:_____	MARKETING HOURS:_____
BRAINSTORMING HOURS:_____	RESEARCH HOURS:_____
EDITING HOURS:_____	READING HOURS:_____

DAILY ACCOMPLISHMENTS	**WEDNESDAY 7**
WORD COUNT:_____	MARKETING HOURS:_____
BRAINSTORMING HOURS:_____	RESEARCH HOURS:_____
EDITING HOURS:_____	READING HOURS:_____

Weekly Overview

Speaker　　　　　Garbage

Post your exercise on the 4HP Accountable Authors Group on Facebook!

What was your sprint time and top word count?

_____

List a new song you discovered this week:

_____

Favorite food or drink this week:

_____

How did you reward yourself?

_____

What project(s) did you work on?

_____

What are you reading?

_____

What went well this week?

_____

What could improve this week?

_____

_____

_____

Total for the Week

Word Count:_____　　Marketing Hours:_____
Brainstorming Hours:_____　Research Hours:_____
Editing Hours:_____　　Reading Hours:_____

Don't forget to color in your grid!

JULY

The Cheerleader

Milestone time:
We are almost halfway through the year. Make sure you are keeping up with tracking your time/activities. It is a little extra work but gives you a glimpse into your accomplishments and future.
Remember: You've got this.

THE ARCHITECT

Feeling blocked? Use this time to do research, organize your notes, or focus on something else project-related, so your mind doesn't wander from the main task: writing.

JULY

THE RESEARCHER

"I'm not a very good writer, but I'm an excellent rewriter."

~ James A. Michener

THE TASKMASTER

Okay. You are officially halfway through the year. How's it going? If you need to change something, do it. You can reset your goals so they are more reasonable, but you can also challenge yourself to surpass new ones.

JULY

WEEK 2

DAILY ACCOMPLISHMENTS	THURSDAY 8
WORD COUNT:	MARKETING HOURS:
BRAINSTORMING HOURS:	RESEARCH HOURS:
EDITING HOURS:	READING HOURS:

DAILY ACCOMPLISHMENTS	FRIDAY 9
WORD COUNT:	MARKETING HOURS:
BRAINSTORMING HOURS:	RESEARCH HOURS:
EDITING HOURS:	READING HOURS:

DAILY ACCOMPLISHMENTS	SATURDAY 10
WORD COUNT:	MARKETING HOURS:
BRAINSTORMING HOURS:	RESEARCH HOURS:
EDITING HOURS:	READING HOURS:

DAILY ACCOMPLISHMENTS	SUNDAY 11
WORD COUNT:	MARKETING HOURS:
BRAINSTORMING HOURS:	RESEARCH HOURS:
EDITING HOURS:	READING HOURS:

DAILY ACCOMPLISHMENTS	MONDAY 12
WORD COUNT:	MARKETING HOURS:
BRAINSTORMING HOURS:	RESEARCH HOURS:
EDITING HOURS:	READING HOURS:

DAILY ACCOMPLISHMENTS	TUESDAY 13
WORD COUNT:	MARKETING HOURS:
BRAINSTORMING HOURS:	RESEARCH HOURS:
EDITING HOURS:	READING HOURS:

DAILY ACCOMPLISHMENTS	WEDNESDAY 14
WORD COUNT:	MARKETING HOURS:
BRAINSTORMING HOURS:	RESEARCH HOURS:
EDITING HOURS:	READING HOURS:

Exercise: Take 5-minute to write something with the 2 words below:

Paper   Bike

Post your exercise on the 4HP Accountable Authors Group on Facebook!

What was your sprint time and top word count?

_____

List a new song you discovered this week:

_____

Favorite food or drink this week:

_____

How did you reward yourself?

_____

What project(s) did you work on?

_____

What are you reading?

_____

What went well this week?

_____

What could improve this week?

_____

_____

_____

Total for the Week

Word Count:_____   Marketing Hours:_____
Brainstorming Hours:_____   Research Hours:_____
Editing Hours:_____   Reading Hours:_____

Don't forget to color in your grid!

JULY

The Cheerleader

"The man who does not read books has no advantage over the man that cannot read them."

~ Mark Twain

JULY

THE ARCHITECT

Plot Holes Everywhere: Fill in the gaps. Think about the downtime between events in your project. How can you use these moments to build character, develop themes, or propel your story forward?

THE RESEARCHER

Pick a color that describes the mood of your lead charater right now! What is it?

THE TASKMASTER

Are you jealous of other writers' accomplishments? Trust me--there're those who are jealous of you. Remember, you're someone else's inspiration; you just might not see it yet.

JULY

139

WEEK 3

DAILY ACCOMPLISHMENTS	THURSDAY 15
WORD COUNT:	MARKETING HOURS:
BRAINSTORMING HOURS:	RESEARCH HOURS:
EDITING HOURS:	READING HOURS:

DAILY ACCOMPLISHMENTS	FRIDAY 16
WORD COUNT:	MARKETING HOURS:
BRAINSTORMING HOURS:	RESEARCH HOURS:
EDITING HOURS:	READING HOURS:

DAILY ACCOMPLISHMENTS	SATURDAY 17
WORD COUNT:	MARKETING HOURS:
BRAINSTORMING HOURS:	RESEARCH HOURS:
EDITING HOURS:	READING HOURS:

DAILY ACCOMPLISHMENTS	SUNDAY 18
WORD COUNT:	MARKETING HOURS:
BRAINSTORMING HOURS:	RESEARCH HOURS:
EDITING HOURS:	READING HOURS:

DAILY ACCOMPLISHMENTS	MONDAY 19
WORD COUNT:	MARKETING HOURS:
BRAINSTORMING HOURS:	RESEARCH HOURS:
EDITING HOURS:	READING HOURS:

DAILY ACCOMPLISHMENTS	TUESDAY 20
WORD COUNT:	MARKETING HOURS:
BRAINSTORMING HOURS:	RESEARCH HOURS:
EDITING HOURS:	READING HOURS:

DAILY ACCOMPLISHMENTS	WEDNESDAY 21
WORD COUNT:	MARKETING HOURS:
BRAINSTORMING HOURS:	RESEARCH HOURS:
EDITING HOURS:	READING HOURS:

WEEKLY OVERVIEW

EXERCISE: Take 5-minute to write something with the 2 words below:

Stamp   Fan

Post your exercise on the 4HP Accountable Authors Group on Facebook!

What was your sprint time and top word count?

_____

List a new song you discovered this week:

_____

Favorite food or drink this week:

_____

How did you reward yourself?

_____

What project(s) did you work on?

_____

What are you reading?

_____

What went well this week?

_____

What could improve this week?

_____

_____

_____

TOTAL FOR THE WEEK

Word Count:_____   Marketing Hours:_____
Brainstorming Hours:_____   Research Hours:_____
Editing Hours:_____   Reading Hours:_____

Don't forget to color in your grid!

JULY

The Cheerleader

Social Media Time: Pay attention to the real world besides your project. Post meaningful content on social media that relates to your writing (*share a book, link an article, post a meme, etc.*)

THE ARCHITECT

"Don't be 'a writer.' Be writing."
~ William Faukner

THE RESEARCHER

Use multiple sources to find tid bits for your current research topic. Don't trust everything you read on the internet.

THE TASKMASTER

About three things I am absolutely certain: You are awesome! You can reach your goals! And fans hunger for your words! Never lose sight of that. (*And Edward is a vampire.*)

Week 4

DAILY ACCOMPLISHMENTS	THURSDAY 22
WORD COUNT:	MARKETING HOURS:
BRAINSTORMING HOURS:	RESEARCH HOURS:
EDITING HOURS:	READING HOURS:

DAILY ACCOMPLISHMENTS	FRIDAY 23
WORD COUNT:	MARKETING HOURS:
BRAINSTORMING HOURS:	RESEARCH HOURS:
EDITING HOURS:	READING HOURS:

DAILY ACCOMPLISHMENTS	SATURDAY 24
WORD COUNT:	MARKETING HOURS:
BRAINSTORMING HOURS:	RESEARCH HOURS:
EDITING HOURS:	READING HOURS:

DAILY ACCOMPLISHMENTS	SUNDAY 25
WORD COUNT:	MARKETING HOURS:
BRAINSTORMING HOURS:	RESEARCH HOURS:
EDITING HOURS:	READING HOURS:

DAILY ACCOMPLISHMENTS	MONDAY 26
WORD COUNT:	MARKETING HOURS:
BRAINSTORMING HOURS:	RESEARCH HOURS:
EDITING HOURS:	READING HOURS:

DAILY ACCOMPLISHMENTS	TUESDAY 27
WORD COUNT:	MARKETING HOURS:
BRAINSTORMING HOURS:	RESEARCH HOURS:
EDITING HOURS:	READING HOURS:

DAILY ACCOMPLISHMENTS	WEDNESDAY 28
WORD COUNT:	MARKETING HOURS:
BRAINSTORMING HOURS:	RESEARCH HOURS:
EDITING HOURS:	READING HOURS:

Weekly Overview

What was your sprint time and top word count?

_____

List a new song you discovered this week:

_____

Favorite food or drink this week:

_____

How did you reward yourself?

_____

What project(s) did you work on?

_____

What are you reading?

_____

What went well this week?

_____

What could improve this week?

_____

_____

_____

JULY

Total for the Week

Word Count:_____ Marketing Hours:_____
Brainstorming Hours:_____ Research Hours:_____
Editing Hours:_____ Reading Hours:_____

Don't forget to color in your grid!

The Cheerleader

Find someone who overcame a challenge. Screenshot their picture. Make it the background image on your phone for a day.

THE ARCHITECT

Summary Check-in: Review your current project's summary. Does it still reflect the current iteration of your project?

THE RESEARCHER

"The role of a writer is not to say what we all can say, but what we are unable to say."

~ Anaïs Nin

THE TASKMASTER

Find your top word count day. Then take a day this week and write more than that. Your abilities will amaze you if you stop doubting them.

JULY

147

DAILY ACCOMPLISHMENTS	THURSDAY 29
WORD COUNT:	MARKETING HOURS:
BRAINSTORMING HOURS:	RESEARCH HOURS:
EDITING HOURS:	READING HOURS:

DAILY ACCOMPLISHMENTS	FRIDAY 30
WORD COUNT:	MARKETING HOURS:
BRAINSTORMING HOURS:	RESEARCH HOURS:
EDITING HOURS:	READING HOURS:

DAILY ACCOMPLISHMENTS	SATURDAY 31
WORD COUNT:	MARKETING HOURS:
BRAINSTORMING HOURS:	RESEARCH HOURS:
EDITING HOURS:	READING HOURS:

JULY

THE ARCHITECT

It's time to declare your independence from bad habits and wasted time. It is easy to get distracted. Make sure you and your project are a priority. Have you been doing your sprints? If not, this is a good time to add them to your schedule.

WEEKLY OVERVIEW

EXERCISE: Take 5-minute to write something with the 2 words below:

Finish   Gold

Post your exercise on the 4HP Accountable Authors Group on Facebook!

What was your sprint time and top word count?

_____

List a new song you discovered this week:

_____

Favorite food or drink this week:

_____

How did you reward yourself?

_____

What project(s) did you work on?

_____

What are you reading?

_____

What went well this week?

_____

What could improve this week?

_____

_____

_____

TOTAL FOR THE WEEK

Word Count:_____   Marketing Hours:_____
Brainstorming Hours:_____   Research Hours:_____
Editing Hours:_____   Reading Hours:_____

Don't forget to color in your grid!

MONTHLY ACTIVITY GRID

JULY

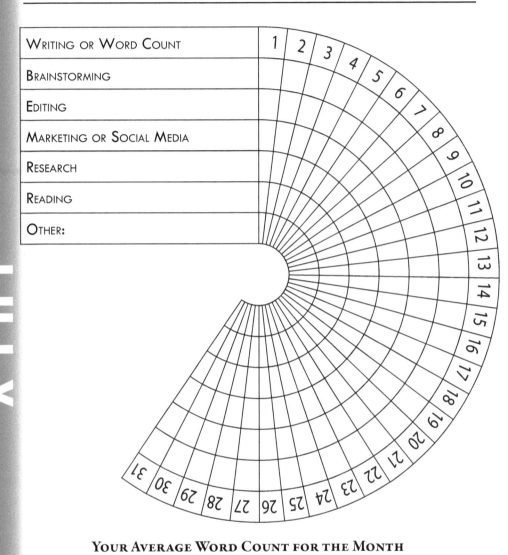

WRITING OR WORD COUNT	1 2 3 4 5 6 7 8 9 10 11 12 13 14 15 16 17 18 19 20 21 22 23 24 25 26 27 28 29 30 31
BRAINSTORMING	
EDITING	
MARKETING OR SOCIAL MEDIA	
RESEARCH	
READING	
OTHER:	

YOUR AVERAGE WORD COUNT FOR THE MONTH

Total Word Count:_____ Divided by _____ days =_____

TOTAL FOR THE YEAR SO FAR

Word Count:_____   Marketing Hours:_____
Brainstorming Hours:_____   Research Hours:_____
Editing Hours:_____   Reading Hours:_____

JOURNAL

JULY

What was your **top week**?

_____

What made your **top week** successful?

_____

What was your biggest **obstacle**?

_____

How did you **overcome** this? Or could do better next time?

_____

_____

What was your biggest **achievement**?

_____

_____

What **inspired** you most this month?

_____

Did you **discover** a new writing tip or advice this month?

_____

_____

TOTAL FOR THE MONTH

Word Count:_____   Research Hours:_____
Brainstorming Hours:_____   Reading Hours:_____
Editing Hours:_____
Marketing Hours:_____

TOTAL FOR THE YEAR SO FAR

Word Count:_____   Research Hours:_____
Brainstorming Hours:_____   Reading Hours:_____
Editing Hours:_____
Marketing Hours:_____

Don't forget to color in your grid!

AUGUST

S chool is coming soon. Have you thought about some creative writing classes? You do not have to be "in college" to take them. Also, you can find different writing workshops both online and in person. Knowledge is power. Make sure you are constantly learning even more skills as an author.

School is Starting!

WHAT DOES YOUR MONTH LOOK LIKE

Holidays:_____   Weekends:_____
Weekdays:_____   Other:_____

What **project(s)** do you plan on working on?

_____

What **goal** are you aiming to achieve?

_____

What will be your biggest **obstacle** this month?

_____

How will you **overcome** this? Or adjust for this?

_____

What will be your End of the Month **reward**?

_____

GOALS FOR THIS MONTH

Word Count:_____   Marketing Hours:_____
Brainstorming Hours:_____   Research Hours:_____
Editing Hours:_____   Reading Hours:_____

Week 1

DAILY ACCOMPLISHMENTS	SUNDAY 1

WORD COUNT:_____ MARKETING HOURS:_____
BRAINSTORMING HOURS:_____ RESEARCH HOURS:_____
EDITING HOURS:_____ READING HOURS:_____

DAILY ACCOMPLISHMENTS	MONDAY 2

WORD COUNT:_____ MARKETING HOURS:_____
BRAINSTORMING HOURS:_____ RESEARCH HOURS:_____
EDITING HOURS:_____ READING HOURS:_____

DAILY ACCOMPLISHMENTS	TUESDAY 3

WORD COUNT:_____ MARKETING HOURS:_____
BRAINSTORMING HOURS:_____ RESEARCH HOURS:_____
EDITING HOURS:_____ READING HOURS:_____

DAILY ACCOMPLISHMENTS	WEDNESDAY 4

WORD COUNT:_____ MARKETING HOURS:_____
BRAINSTORMING HOURS:_____ RESEARCH HOURS:_____
EDITING HOURS:_____ READING HOURS:_____

DAILY ACCOMPLISHMENTS	THURSDAY 5

WORD COUNT:_____ MARKETING HOURS:_____
BRAINSTORMING HOURS:_____ RESEARCH HOURS:_____
EDITING HOURS:_____ READING HOURS:_____

DAILY ACCOMPLISHMENTS	FRIDAY 6

WORD COUNT:_____ MARKETING HOURS:_____
BRAINSTORMING HOURS:_____ RESEARCH HOURS:_____
EDITING HOURS:_____ READING HOURS:_____

DAILY ACCOMPLISHMENTS	SATURDAY 7

WORD COUNT:_____ MARKETING HOURS:_____
BRAINSTORMING HOURS:_____ RESEARCH HOURS:_____
EDITING HOURS:_____ READING HOURS:_____

WEEKLY OVERVIEW

EXERCISE: Take 5-minute to write something with the 2 words below:

Stare   Can

Post your exercise on the 4HP Accountable Authors Group on Facebook!

What was your sprint time and top word count?

_____

List a new song you discovered this week:

_____

Favorite food or drink this week:

_____

How did you reward yourself?

_____

What project(s) did you work on?

_____

What are you reading?

_____

What went well this week?

_____

What could improve this week?

_____

_____

_____

TOTAL FOR THE WEEK

Word Count:_____   Marketing Hours:_____
Brainstorming Hours:_____   Research Hours:_____
Editing Hours:_____   Reading Hours:_____

Don't forget to color in your grid!

The Cheerleader

Best book to movie adaption. Justify it.

THE ARCHITECT

Eliminate passive voice as much as possible. Passive: This fantasy novel was written by Vanessa. Active: Vanessa wrote a fantasy novel.

THE RESEARCHER

Are you writing about fossils? Blood spatter? Cuisine? Find an expert in that field and ask them to speak with you. You will be surprised how much they're willing to share.

THE TASKMASTER

Every day, do something that scares you. Comfort zones make you complacent. Life is an adventure; don't wait for it to come to you.

AUGUST

Week 2

Daily Accomplishments — Sunday 8

Word Count:_____

Brainstorming Hours:_____

Editing Hours:_____

Marketing Hours:_____

Research Hours:_____

Reading Hours:_____

Daily Accomplishments — Monday 9

Word Count:_____

Brainstorming Hours:_____

Editing Hours:_____

Marketing Hours:_____

Research Hours:_____

Reading Hours:_____

Daily Accomplishments — Tuesday 10

Word Count:_____

Brainstorming Hours:_____

Editing Hours:_____

Marketing Hours:_____

Research Hours:_____

Reading Hours:_____

Daily Accomplishments — Wednesday 11

Word Count:_____

Brainstorming Hours:_____

Editing Hours:_____

Marketing Hours:_____

Research Hours:_____

Reading Hours:_____

Daily Accomplishments — Thursday 12

Word Count:_____

Brainstorming Hours:_____

Editing Hours:_____

Marketing Hours:_____

Research Hours:_____

Reading Hours:_____

Daily Accomplishments — Friday 13

Word Count:_____

Brainstorming Hours:_____

Editing Hours:_____

Marketing Hours:_____

Research Hours:_____

Reading Hours:_____

Daily Accomplishments — Saturday 14

Word Count:_____

Brainstorming Hours:_____

Editing Hours:_____

Marketing Hours:_____

Research Hours:_____

Reading Hours:_____

AUGUST

Weekly Overview

EXERCISE: Take 5-minute to write something with the 2 words below:

Pop   Knee

Post your exercise on the 4HP Accountable Authors Group on Facebook!

What was your sprint time and top word count?

_____

List a new song you discovered this week:

_____

Favorite food or drink this week:

_____

How did you reward yourself?

_____

What project(s) did you work on?

_____

What are you reading?

_____

What went well this week?

_____

What could improve this week?

_____

_____

_____

Total for the Week

Word Count:_____   Marketing Hours:_____
Brainstorming Hours:_____   Research Hours:_____
Editing Hours:_____   Reading Hours:_____

Don't forget to color in your grid!

The Cheerleader

"Do or do not. There is no try."
~ Yoda (Star Wars)

AUGUST

THE ARCHITECT

Bio Update:
　　Review your author
　　biography.
　　Tweak for changes.
　　Keep it up to date often!

THE RESEARCHER

Wordbuilding is fun because you can create all the rules. But don't forget to write them down. Be consistent.

THE TASKMASTER

When was the last time you read your writing out loud? Find an open mic and go and read. You may be nervous but hearing your words out loud is a very good idea.

AUGUST

AUGUST

DAILY ACCOMPLISHMENTS · SUNDAY 15

Word Count: _____
Brainstorming Hours: _____
Editing Hours: _____

Marketing Hours: _____
Research Hours: _____
Reading Hours: _____

DAILY ACCOMPLISHMENTS · MONDAY 16

Word Count: _____
Brainstorming Hours: _____
Editing Hours: _____

Marketing Hours: _____
Research Hours: _____
Reading Hours: _____

DAILY ACCOMPLISHMENTS · TUESDAY 17

Word Count: _____
Brainstorming Hours: _____
Editing Hours: _____

Marketing Hours: _____
Research Hours: _____
Reading Hours: _____

DAILY ACCOMPLISHMENTS · WEDNESDAY 18

Word Count: _____
Brainstorming Hours: _____
Editing Hours: _____

Marketing Hours: _____
Research Hours: _____
Reading Hours: _____

DAILY ACCOMPLISHMENTS · THURSDAY 19

Word Count: _____
Brainstorming Hours: _____
Editing Hours: _____

Marketing Hours: _____
Research Hours: _____
Reading Hours: _____

DAILY ACCOMPLISHMENTS · FRIDAY 20

Word Count: _____
Brainstorming Hours: _____
Editing Hours: _____

Marketing Hours: _____
Research Hours: _____
Reading Hours: _____

DAILY ACCOMPLISHMENTS · SATURDAY 21

Word Count: _____
Brainstorming Hours: _____
Editing Hours: _____

Marketing Hours: _____
Research Hours: _____
Reading Hours: _____

WEEKLY OVERVIEW

EXERCISE: Take 5-minute to write something with the 2 words below:

Finger   Blind

Post your exercise on the 4HP Accountable Authors Group on Facebook!

What was your sprint time and top word count?

_____

List a new song you discovered this week:

_____

Favorite food or drink this week:

_____

How did you reward yourself?

_____

What project(s) did you work on?

_____

What are you reading?

_____

What went well this week?

_____

What could improve this week?

_____

_____

_____

TOTAL FOR THE WEEK

Word Count:_____   Marketing Hours:_____
Brainstorming Hours:_____   Research Hours:_____
Editing Hours:_____   Reading Hours:_____

Don't forget to color in your grid!

The Cheerleader

"E.L. Doctorow said once said that 'Writing a novel is like driving a car at night. You can see only as far as your headlights, but you can make the whole trip that way.' You don't have to see where you're going; you don't have to see your destination or everything you will pass along the way. You just have to see two or three feet ahead of you. This is right up there with the best advice on writing, or life, I have ever heard."

~Anne Lamott (Bird by Bird: Some Instructions on Writing and Life)

THE ARCHITECT

"Don't wait for the right opportunity: create it."

~ George Bernard Shaw

THE RESEARCHER

Interview Time: Create a list of questions you'd like to ask a character in your project.

THE TASKMASTER

What's your worst fear as a writer? Write it down on paper. Then rip it to shreds. Or burn it. Good--you're done with that now. Move forward.

AUGUST

DAILY ACCOMPLISHMENTS   **SUNDAY 22**

WORD COUNT:_____   MARKETING HOURS:_____
BRAINSTORMING HOURS:_____ RESEARCH HOURS:_____
EDITING HOURS:_____   READING HOURS:_____

DAILY ACCOMPLISHMENTS   **MONDAY 23**

WORD COUNT:_____   MARKETING HOURS:_____
BRAINSTORMING HOURS:_____ RESEARCH HOURS:_____
EDITING HOURS:_____   READING HOURS:_____

DAILY ACCOMPLISHMENTS   **TUESDAY 24**

WORD COUNT:_____   MARKETING HOURS:_____
BRAINSTORMING HOURS:_____ RESEARCH HOURS:_____
EDITING HOURS:_____   READING HOURS:_____

DAILY ACCOMPLISHMENTS   **WEDNESDAY 25**

WORD COUNT:_____   MARKETING HOURS:_____
BRAINSTORMING HOURS:_____ RESEARCH HOURS:_____
EDITING HOURS:_____   READING HOURS:_____

DAILY ACCOMPLISHMENTS   **THURSDAY 26**

WORD COUNT:_____   MARKETING HOURS:_____
BRAINSTORMING HOURS:_____ RESEARCH HOURS:_____
EDITING HOURS:_____   READING HOURS:_____

DAILY ACCOMPLISHMENTS   **FRIDAY 27**

WORD COUNT:_____   MARKETING HOURS:_____
BRAINSTORMING HOURS:_____ RESEARCH HOURS:_____
EDITING HOURS:_____   READING HOURS:_____

DAILY ACCOMPLISHMENTS   **SATURDAY 28**

WORD COUNT:_____   MARKETING HOURS:_____
BRAINSTORMING HOURS:_____ RESEARCH HOURS:_____
EDITING HOURS:_____   READING HOURS:_____

AUGUST

WEEKLY OVERVIEW

EXERCISE: Take 5-minute to write something with the 2 words below:

Movement   Papaya

Post your exercise on the 4HP Accountable Authors Group on Facebook!

What was your sprint time and top word count?

_____

List a new song you discovered this week:

_____

Favorite food or drink this week:

_____

How did you reward yourself?

_____

What project(s) did you work on?

_____

What are you reading?

_____

What went well this week?

_____

What could improve this week?

_____

_____

_____

TOTAL FOR THE WEEK

Word Count:_____   Marketing Hours:_____
Brainstorming Hours:_____   Research Hours:_____
Editing Hours:_____   Reading Hours:_____

Don't forget to color in your grid!

The Cheerleader

Focus on editing your work once this week. How is it coming along?

THE ARCHITECT

If you're writing about something outside of your experience, make sure to have several beta readers of that particular group read and critique. Example: Male writing from a female POV. Straight person writing from an LGBTQ+ POV, etc.

THE RESEARCHER

A hand-drawn map of the town or area your characters are in can help you keep the timing and distance straight. This will fit into your project's series guide. Plus, coloring is fun!

THE TASKMASTER

Remember, you will find that people like to share stories. If you're writing about someone from a differen't background or place, then find someone from there and ask questions. Make your charaters feel more real.

AUGUST

DAILY ACCOMPLISHMENTS — SUNDAY 29

WORD COUNT:_____ MARKETING HOURS:_____
BRAINSTORMING HOURS:_____ RESEARCH HOURS:_____
EDITING HOURS:_____ READING HOURS:_____

DAILY ACCOMPLISHMENTS — MONDAY 30

WORD COUNT:_____ MARKETING HOURS:_____
BRAINSTORMING HOURS:_____ RESEARCH HOURS:_____
EDITING HOURS:_____ READING HOURS:_____

DAILY ACCOMPLISHMENTS — TUESDAY 31

WORD COUNT:_____ MARKETING HOURS:_____
BRAINSTORMING HOURS:_____ RESEARCH HOURS:_____
EDITING HOURS:_____ READING HOURS:_____

THE RESEARCHER

The beginning of fall is fast approaching. Make sure not to fall back on your writing. See what I did there? A pun just for you! How is your knowledge acquistion going? Are you spending time learning some tricks of the trade that you can apply? Good if you are, and you'd better get that going if you are not! This is all about you.

AUGUST

WEEKLY OVERVIEW

EXERCISE: Take 5-minute to write something with the 2 words below:

Gang   Fish

Post your exercise on the 4HP Accountable Authors Group on Facebook!

What was your sprint time and top word count?

_____

List a new song you discovered this week:

_____

Favorite food or drink this week:

_____

How did you reward yourself?

_____

What project(s) did you work on?

_____

What are you reading?

_____

What went well this week?

_____

What could improve this week?

_____

_____

_____

TOTAL FOR THE WEEK

Word Count:_____   Marketing Hours:_____
Brainstorming Hours:_____   Research Hours:_____
Editing Hours:_____   Reading Hours:_____

Don't forget to color in your grid!

MONTHLY ACTIVITY GRID

AUGUST

WRITING OR WORD COUNT
BRAINSTORMING
EDITING
MARKETING OR SOCIAL MEDIA
RESEARCH
READING
OTHER:

1 2 3 4 5 6 7 8 9 10 11 12 13 14 15 16 17 18 19 20 21 22 23 24 25 26 27 28 29 30 31

YOUR AVERAGE WORD COUNT FOR THE MONTH

Total Word Count:_____ Divided by _____ days =_____

TOTAL FOR THE YEAR SO FAR

Word Count:_____
Brainstorming Hours:_____
Editing Hours:_____

Marketing Hours:_____
Research Hours:_____
Reading Hours:_____

Journal

AUGUST

AUGUST

What was your **top week**?

_____

What made your **top week** successful?

_____

What was your biggest **obstacle**?

_____

How did you **overcome** this? Or could do better next time?

_____

_____

What was your biggest **achievement**?

_____

_____

What **inspired** you most this month?

_____

Did you **discover** a new writing tip or advice this month?

_____

_____

TOTAL FOR THE MONTH

Word Count:_____   Research Hours:_____
Brainstorming Hours:_____   Reading Hours:_____
Editing Hours:_____
Marketing Hours:_____

TOTAL FOR THE YEAR SO FAR

Word Count:_____   Research Hours:_____
Brainstorming Hours:_____   Reading Hours:_____
Editing Hours:_____
Marketing Hours:_____

Don't forget to color in your grid!

September

School has started again. You might be one of the many hitting the books or helping others to do so. Make sure you do not lose the good habits you formed. Also, this is a great time to find a local writers group. Finding like-minded people in your area or online is one of the most helpful things you can do. Also, don't forget to buy your 2022 Authors Accountability Guide!

Sept. 6th - Labor Day

What Does Your Month Look Like

Holidays:_____   Weekends:_____

Weekdays:_____   Other:_____

What **project(s)** do you plan on working on?

_____

What **goal** are you aiming to achieve?

_____

What will be your biggest **obstacle** this month?

_____

How will you **overcome** this? Or adjust for this?

_____

What will be your End of the Month **reward**?

_____

Goals for this Month

Word Count:_____   Marketing Hours:_____

Brainstorming Hours:_____   Research Hours:_____

Editing Hours:_____   Reading Hours:_____

WEEK 1

DAILY ACCOMPLISHMENTS	**WEDNESDAY 1**
WORD COUNT:_____	MARKETING HOURS:_____
BRAINSTORMING HOURS:_____	RESEARCH HOURS:_____
EDITING HOURS:_____	READING HOURS:_____

DAILY ACCOMPLISHMENTS	**THURSDAY 2**
WORD COUNT:_____	MARKETING HOURS:_____
BRAINSTORMING HOURS:_____	RESEARCH HOURS:_____
EDITING HOURS:_____	READING HOURS:_____

DAILY ACCOMPLISHMENTS	**FRIDAY 3**
WORD COUNT:_____	MARKETING HOURS:_____
BRAINSTORMING HOURS:_____	RESEARCH HOURS:_____
EDITING HOURS:_____	READING HOURS:_____

DAILY ACCOMPLISHMENTS	**SATURDAY 4**
WORD COUNT:_____	MARKETING HOURS:_____
BRAINSTORMING HOURS:_____	RESEARCH HOURS:_____
EDITING HOURS:_____	READING HOURS:_____

DAILY ACCOMPLISHMENTS	**SUNDAY 5**
WORD COUNT:_____	MARKETING HOURS:_____
BRAINSTORMING HOURS:_____	RESEARCH HOURS:_____
EDITING HOURS:_____	READING HOURS:_____

DAILY ACCOMPLISHMENTS	**MONDAY 6**
WORD COUNT:_____	MARKETING HOURS:_____
BRAINSTORMING HOURS:_____	RESEARCH HOURS:_____
EDITING HOURS:_____	READING HOURS:_____

DAILY ACCOMPLISHMENTS	**TUESDAY 7**
WORD COUNT:_____	MARKETING HOURS:_____
BRAINSTORMING HOURS:_____	RESEARCH HOURS:_____
EDITING HOURS:_____	READING HOURS:_____

EXERCISE: Take 5-minute to write something with the 2 words below:

Circle   Breath

Post your exercise on the 4HP Accountable Authors Group on Facebook!

What was your sprint time and top word count?

_____

List a new song you discovered this week:

_____

Favorite food or drink this week:

_____

How did you reward yourself?

_____

What project(s) did you work on?

_____

What are you reading?

_____

What went well this week?

_____

What could improve this week?

_____

_____

_____

TOTAL FOR THE WEEK

Word Count:_____   Marketing Hours:_____
Brainstorming Hours:_____   Research Hours:_____
Editing Hours:_____   Reading Hours:_____

Don't forget to color in your grid!

SEPTEMBER

The Cheerleader

Write in a different place once this week. How did it go?

THE ARCHITECT

"My perfect day is sitting in a room with some blank paper. That's heaven. That's gold and anything else is just a waste of time."

~ Cormac McCarthy

SEPTEMBER

THE RESEARCHER

The Roman Naval fleet lost most of its ships during the same earthquake that knocked Helike into the sea! Set a timer for 10 minutes and write a scene or poem with an earthquake.

THE TASKMASTER

Did you know Bill Gates recommends using five hours a week to continue learning? You can always gain more knowledge about your craft. Start a book on writing by a successful writer, take a webinar, or listen to a podcast.

SEPTEMBER

Week 2

DAILY ACCOMPLISHMENTS   **WEDNESDAY 8**

WORD COUNT:_____   MARKETING HOURS:_____
BRAINSTORMING HOURS:_____   RESEARCH HOURS:_____
EDITING HOURS:_____   READING HOURS:_____

DAILY ACCOMPLISHMENTS   **THURSDAY 9**

WORD COUNT:_____   MARKETING HOURS:_____
BRAINSTORMING HOURS:_____   RESEARCH HOURS:_____
EDITING HOURS:_____   READING HOURS:_____

DAILY ACCOMPLISHMENTS   **FRIDAY 10**

WORD COUNT:_____   MARKETING HOURS:_____
BRAINSTORMING HOURS:_____   RESEARCH HOURS:_____
EDITING HOURS:_____   READING HOURS:_____

DAILY ACCOMPLISHMENTS   **SATURDAY 11**

WORD COUNT:_____   MARKETING HOURS:_____
BRAINSTORMING HOURS:_____   RESEARCH HOURS:_____
EDITING HOURS:_____   READING HOURS:_____

DAILY ACCOMPLISHMENTS   **SUNDAY 12**

WORD COUNT:_____   MARKETING HOURS:_____
BRAINSTORMING HOURS:_____   RESEARCH HOURS:_____
EDITING HOURS:_____   READING HOURS:_____

DAILY ACCOMPLISHMENTS   **MONDAY 13**

WORD COUNT:_____   MARKETING HOURS:_____
BRAINSTORMING HOURS:_____   RESEARCH HOURS:_____
EDITING HOURS:_____   READING HOURS:_____

DAILY ACCOMPLISHMENTS   **TUESDAY 14**

WORD COUNT:_____   MARKETING HOURS:_____
BRAINSTORMING HOURS:_____   RESEARCH HOURS:_____
EDITING HOURS:_____   READING HOURS:_____

WEEKLY OVERVIEW

EXERCISE: Take 5-minute to write something with the 2 words below:

Knuckle　　　　　Stock

Post your exercise on the 4HP Accountable Authors Group on Facebook!

What was your sprint time and top word count?

_____

List a new song you discovered this week:

_____

Favorite food or drink this week:

_____

How did you reward yourself?

_____

What project(s) did you work on?

_____

What are you reading?

_____

What went well this week?

_____

What could improve this week?

_____

_____

_____

TOTAL FOR THE WEEK

Word Count:_____   Marketing Hours:_____
Brainstorming Hours:_____   Research Hours:_____
Editing Hours:_____   Reading Hours:_____

Don't forget to color in your grid!

The Cheerleader

"I cannot say this often enough: if your backstory is more interesting than your current era, you're writing the wrong story."

~ Lynn Viehl

THE ARCHITECT

Switch gears and work on a different project this week. How did it go?

THE RESEARCHER

Vocab Building Time: Learn five new words. Flip through a dictionary, scroll through an online dictionary--whatever works for you.

THE TASKMASTER

Don't "*try*" to write. Just write! It's that simple. Even if you have to put aside your current project, write a piece of flash fiction or do another exercise--just continue to be creative.

SEPTEMBER

WEEK 3

DAILY ACCOMPLISHMENTS   **WEDNESDAY 15**

WORD COUNT:_____

BRAINSTORMING HOURS:_____

EDITING HOURS:_____

MARKETING HOURS:_____

RESEARCH HOURS:_____

READING HOURS:_____

DAILY ACCOMPLISHMENTS   **THURSDAY 16**

WORD COUNT:_____

BRAINSTORMING HOURS:_____

EDITING HOURS:_____

MARKETING HOURS:_____

RESEARCH HOURS:_____

READING HOURS:_____

DAILY ACCOMPLISHMENTS   **FRIDAY 17**

WORD COUNT:_____

BRAINSTORMING HOURS:_____

EDITING HOURS:_____

MARKETING HOURS:_____

RESEARCH HOURS:_____

READING HOURS:_____

DAILY ACCOMPLISHMENTS   **SATURDAY 18**

WORD COUNT:_____

BRAINSTORMING HOURS:_____

EDITING HOURS:_____

MARKETING HOURS:_____

RESEARCH HOURS:_____

READING HOURS:_____

DAILY ACCOMPLISHMENTS   **SUNDAY 19**

WORD COUNT:_____

BRAINSTORMING HOURS:_____

EDITING HOURS:_____

MARKETING HOURS:_____

RESEARCH HOURS:_____

READING HOURS:_____

DAILY ACCOMPLISHMENTS   **MONDAY 20**

WORD COUNT:_____

BRAINSTORMING HOURS:_____

EDITING HOURS:_____

MARKETING HOURS:_____

RESEARCH HOURS:_____

READING HOURS:_____

DAILY ACCOMPLISHMENTS   **TUESDAY 21**

WORD COUNT:_____

BRAINSTORMING HOURS:_____

EDITING HOURS:_____

MARKETING HOURS:_____

RESEARCH HOURS:_____

READING HOURS:_____

WEEKLY OVERVIEW

EXERCISE: Take 5-minute to write something with the 2 words below:

Toadstool   Pavement

Post your exercise on the 4HP Accountable Authors Group on Facebook!

What was your sprint time and top word count?

_____

List a new song you discovered this week:

_____

Favorite food or drink this week:

_____

How did you reward yourself?

_____

What project(s) did you work on?

_____

What are you reading?

_____

What went well this week?

_____

What could improve this week?

_____

_____

_____

TOTAL FOR THE WEEK

Word Count:_____   Marketing Hours:_____
Brainstorming Hours:_____   Research Hours:_____
Editing Hours:_____   Reading Hours:_____

Don't forget to color in your grid!

SEPTEMBER

The Cheerleader

Write a piece of flash fiction (1000 words or less) and post it on your social media. Put the title here.

THE ARCHITECT

"Ideas are cheap. I have more ideas now than I could ever write up. To my mind, it's the execution that is all-important."

~ George R.R. Martin

THE RESEARCHER

Worst book to movie adaption. Eviscerate it.

THE TASKMASTER

If you're wondering if you're writing enough, the answer is no. Your fans want more from you. Give it to them.

SEPTEMBER

Week 4

DAILY ACCOMPLISHMENTS   WEDNESDAY 22

WORD COUNT:_____   MARKETING HOURS:_____
BRAINSTORMING HOURS:_____ RESEARCH HOURS:_____
EDITING HOURS:_____   READING HOURS:_____

DAILY ACCOMPLISHMENTS   THURSDAY 23

WORD COUNT:_____   MARKETING HOURS:_____
BRAINSTORMING HOURS:_____ RESEARCH HOURS:_____
EDITING HOURS:_____   READING HOURS:_____

DAILY ACCOMPLISHMENTS   FRIDAY 24

WORD COUNT:_____   MARKETING HOURS:_____
BRAINSTORMING HOURS:_____ RESEARCH HOURS:_____
EDITING HOURS:_____   READING HOURS:_____

DAILY ACCOMPLISHMENTS   SATURDAY 25

WORD COUNT:_____   MARKETING HOURS:_____
BRAINSTORMING HOURS:_____ RESEARCH HOURS:_____
EDITING HOURS:_____   READING HOURS:_____

DAILY ACCOMPLISHMENTS   SUNDAY 26

WORD COUNT:_____   MARKETING HOURS:_____
BRAINSTORMING HOURS:_____ RESEARCH HOURS:_____
EDITING HOURS:_____   READING HOURS:_____

DAILY ACCOMPLISHMENTS   MONDAY 27

WORD COUNT:_____   MARKETING HOURS:_____
BRAINSTORMING HOURS:_____ RESEARCH HOURS:_____
EDITING HOURS:_____   READING HOURS:_____

DAILY ACCOMPLISHMENTS   TUESDAY 28

WORD COUNT:_____   MARKETING HOURS:_____
BRAINSTORMING HOURS:_____ RESEARCH HOURS:_____
EDITING HOURS:_____   READING HOURS:_____

Weekly Overview

EXERCISE: Take 5-minute to write something with the 2 words below:

Dog   Lasso

Post your exercise on the 4HP Accountable Authors Group on Facebook!

What was your sprint time and top word count?

_____

List a new song you discovered this week:

_____

Favorite food or drink this week:

_____

How did you reward yourself?

_____

What project(s) did you work on?

_____

What are you reading?

_____

What went well this week?

_____

What could improve this week?

_____

_____

_____

TOTAL FOR THE WEEK

Word Count:_____   Marketing Hours:_____
Brainstorming Hours:_____   Research Hours:_____
Editing Hours:_____   Reading Hours:_____

Don't forget to color in your grid!

The Cheerleader

"All we have to decide is what to do with the time that is given to us."
~ *Gandalf (Lord of the Rings)*

THE ARCHITECT

Make every word, every sentence, every character, and every subplot matter to the main plot.

THE RESEARCHER

Write a story about a character or creature that sweats blood. Hippos do!

THE TASKMASTER

Do you believe your writing won't be appreciated by others? Well, you're wrong. If there's an audience for dinosaur romance, there're people ready to hear your story.

SEPTEMBER

191

DAILY ACCOMPLISHMENTS   **WEDNESDAY 29**

WORD COUNT:_____   MARKETING HOURS:_____
BRAINSTORMING HOURS:_____   RESEARCH HOURS:_____
EDITING HOURS:_____   READING HOURS:_____

DAILY ACCOMPLISHMENTS   **THURSDAY 30**

WORD COUNT:_____   MARKETING HOURS:_____
BRAINSTORMING HOURS:_____   RESEARCH HOURS:_____
EDITING HOURS:_____   READING HOURS:_____

THE TASKMASTER

We are nearing the end of the third quarter. Time tends to race away. It is the only commodity you can never get back. Make the most of it! As we are nearing crunch time (*aka the end of the year*), make sure you are taking time for you: a hike in the woods, a bike ride, a beer with a friend, or a bubblebath. Keeping yourself in mind will make the journey that much easier.

SEPTEMBER

WEEKLY OVERVIEW

EXERCISE: Take 5-minute to write something with the 2 words below:

Cow   Moon

Post your exercise on the 4HP Accountable Authors Group on Facebook!

What was your sprint time and top word count?

_____

List a new song you discovered this week:

_____

Favorite food or drink this week:

_____

How did you reward yourself?

_____

What project(s) did you work on?

_____

What are you reading?

_____

What went well this week?

_____

What could improve this week?

_____

_____

_____

TOTAL FOR THE WEEK

Word Count:_____   Marketing Hours:_____
Brainstorming Hours:_____   Research Hours:_____
Editing Hours:_____   Reading Hours:_____

Don't forget to color in your grid!

MONTHLY ACTIVITY GRID

S E P T E M B E R

WRITING OR WORD COUNT	
BRAINSTORMING	
EDITING	
MARKETING OR SOCIAL MEDIA	
RESEARCH	
READING	
OTHER:	

1 2 3 4 5 6 7 8 9 10 11 12 13 14 15 16 17 18 19 20 21 22 23 24 25 26 27 28 29 30 31

YOUR AVERAGE WORD COUNT FOR THE MONTH

Total Word Count:_____ Divided by _____ days =_____

TOTAL FOR THE YEAR SO FAR

Word Count:_____
Brainstorming Hours:_____
Editing Hours:_____

Marketing Hours:_____
Research Hours:_____
Reading Hours:_____

JOURNAL

SEPTEMBER

What was your **top week**?

_____

What made your **top week** successful?

_____

What was your biggest **obstacle**?

_____

How did you **overcome** this? Or could do better next time?

_____

_____

What was your biggest **achievement**?

_____

_____

What **inspired** you most this month?

_____

Did you **discover** a new writing tip or advice this month?

_____

_____

TOTAL FOR THE MONTH

Word Count:_____   Research Hours:_____
Brainstorming Hours:_____   Reading Hours:_____
Editing Hours:_____
Marketing Hours:_____

TOTAL FOR THE YEAR SO FAR

Word Count:_____   Research Hours:_____
Brainstorming Hours:_____   Reading Hours:_____
Editing Hours:_____
Marketing Hours:_____

Don't forget to color in your grid!

OCTOBER

It is the spookiest month of the year--the Muses' favorite holiday: Halloween! Besides wearing costumes and trick-or-treating, they say this is the time when the veil between worlds is the thinnest. This is the time to realize you only have three months left of 2021--and that NANO is one month away. Time to get prepared, grab a pumpkin-spiced latte and as much candy corn as you can stomach, and keep your inner demons at bay.

Oct 11th - Columbus Dayt
Oct 31st - Halloween

WHAT DOES YOUR MONTH LOOK LIKE

Holidays:_____   Weekends:_____
Weekdays:_____   Other:_____

What **project(s)** do you plan on working on?

_____

What **goal** are you aiming to achieve?

_____

What will be your biggest **obstacle** this month?

_____

How will you **overcome** this? Or adjust for this?

_____

What will be your End of the Month **reward**?

_____

GOALS FOR THIS MONTH

Word Count:_____   Marketing Hours:_____
Brainstorming Hours:_____   Research Hours:_____
Editing Hours:_____   Reading Hours:_____

197

Week 1

DAILY ACCOMPLISHMENTS

FRIDAY 1

WORD COUNT:_____
MARKETING HOURS:_____
BRAINSTORMING HOURS:_____
RESEARCH HOURS:_____
EDITING HOURS:_____
READING HOURS:_____

DAILY ACCOMPLISHMENTS

SATURDAY 2

WORD COUNT:_____
MARKETING HOURS:_____
BRAINSTORMING HOURS:_____
RESEARCH HOURS:_____
EDITING HOURS:_____
READING HOURS:_____

DAILY ACCOMPLISHMENTS

SUNDAY 3

WORD COUNT:_____
MARKETING HOURS:_____
BRAINSTORMING HOURS:_____
RESEARCH HOURS:_____
EDITING HOURS:_____
READING HOURS:_____

DAILY ACCOMPLISHMENTS

MONDAY 4

WORD COUNT:_____
MARKETING HOURS:_____
BRAINSTORMING HOURS:_____
RESEARCH HOURS:_____
EDITING HOURS:_____
READING HOURS:_____

DAILY ACCOMPLISHMENTS

TUESDAY 5

WORD COUNT:_____
MARKETING HOURS:_____
BRAINSTORMING HOURS:_____
RESEARCH HOURS:_____
EDITING HOURS:_____
READING HOURS:_____

DAILY ACCOMPLISHMENTS

WEDNESDAY 6

WORD COUNT:_____
MARKETING HOURS:_____
BRAINSTORMING HOURS:_____
RESEARCH HOURS:_____
EDITING HOURS:_____
READING HOURS:_____

DAILY ACCOMPLISHMENTS

THURSDAY 7

WORD COUNT:_____
MARKETING HOURS:_____
BRAINSTORMING HOURS:_____
RESEARCH HOURS:_____
EDITING HOURS:_____
READING HOURS:_____

WEEKLY OVERVIEW

EXERCISE: Take 5-minute to write something with the 2 words below:

Orange   -   Doorknob

Post your exercise on the 4HP Accountable Authors Group on Facebook!

What was your sprint time and top word count?

_____

List a new song you discovered this week:

_____

Favorite food or drink this week:

_____

How did you reward yourself?

_____

What project(s) did you work on?

_____

What are you reading?

_____

What went well this week?

_____

What could improve this week?

_____

_____

_____

TOTAL FOR THE WEEK

Word Count:_____   Marketing Hours:_____
Brainstorming Hours:_____   Research Hours:_____
Editing Hours:_____   Reading Hours:_____

Don't forget to color in your grid!

OCTOBER

The Cheerleader

Don't wait. The timing will never be just right.

THE ARCHITECT

Build a system! Create a money scheme, craft a calendar, draw a family tree, describe the intricacies of how a town operates, or anything else that will maintain your writing focus.

THE RESEARCHER

Every character should have a quirk or specialty. For example, many people don't realize US President Abraham Lincoln only lost once in the 300 wrestling contests he entered! WOW! Oh, and he's was a licensed bartender...

THE TASKMASTER

"The worst enemy to creativity is self-doubt."
~Sylvia Plath

Never doubt what you can accomplish or if it's good enough. You're doing it, and it is fantastic!

OCTOBER

DAILY ACCOMPLISHMENTS   **FRIDAY 8**

WORD COUNT:_____   MARKETING HOURS:_____

BRAINSTORMING HOURS:_____   RESEARCH HOURS:_____

EDITING HOURS:_____   READING HOURS:_____

DAILY ACCOMPLISHMENTS   **SATURDAY 9**

WORD COUNT:_____   MARKETING HOURS:_____

BRAINSTORMING HOURS:_____   RESEARCH HOURS:_____

EDITING HOURS:_____   READING HOURS:_____

DAILY ACCOMPLISHMENTS   **SUNDAY 10**

WORD COUNT:_____   MARKETING HOURS:_____

BRAINSTORMING HOURS:_____   RESEARCH HOURS:_____

EDITING HOURS:_____   READING HOURS:_____

DAILY ACCOMPLISHMENTS   **MONDAY 11**

WORD COUNT:_____   MARKETING HOURS:_____

BRAINSTORMING HOURS:_____   RESEARCH HOURS:_____

EDITING HOURS:_____   READING HOURS:_____

DAILY ACCOMPLISHMENTS   **TUESDAY 12**

WORD COUNT:_____   MARKETING HOURS:_____

BRAINSTORMING HOURS:_____   RESEARCH HOURS:_____

EDITING HOURS:_____   READING HOURS:_____

DAILY ACCOMPLISHMENTS   **WEDNESDAY 13**

WORD COUNT:_____   MARKETING HOURS:_____

BRAINSTORMING HOURS:_____   RESEARCH HOURS:_____

EDITING HOURS:_____   READING HOURS:_____

DAILY ACCOMPLISHMENTS   **THURSDAY 14**

WORD COUNT:_____   MARKETING HOURS:_____

BRAINSTORMING HOURS:_____   RESEARCH HOURS:_____

EDITING HOURS:_____   READING HOURS:_____

OCTOBER

WEEKLY OVERVIEW

EXERCISE: Take 5-minute to write something with the 2 words below:

Scared   Wrench

Post your exercise on the 4HP Accountable Authors Group on Facebook!

What was your sprint time and top word count?

_____

List a new song you discovered this week:

_____

Favorite food or drink this week:

_____

How did you reward yourself?

_____

What project(s) did you work on?

_____

What are you reading?

_____

What went well this week?

_____

What could improve this week?

_____

_____

_____

TOTAL FOR THE WEEK

Word Count:_____   Marketing Hours:_____
Brainstorming Hours:_____   Research Hours:_____
Editing Hours:_____   Reading Hours:_____

Don't forget to color in your grid!

The Cheerleader

You're in the elevator with your dream publisher. In one minute, explain why your project is freaking amazing.

THE ARCHITECT

"You are not your job. You are not how much money you have in the bank. You are not the car you drive. You're not the contents of your wallet. You are not your fu*king khakis. You are all the singing, all the dancing crap of the world."

~ Chuck Palahniuk (Fight Club)

THE RESEARCHER

Mention a remedy, like medicine or a condiment, in your story. Did you know that in the 1830's, doctors prescribed ketchup as a cure for indigestion?

THE TASKMASTER

Every mistake is a learning experience. Mistakes teach us to do better next time.

OCTOBER

DAILY ACCOMPLISHMENTS   **FRIDAY 15**

WORD COUNT:_____   MARKETING HOURS:_____
BRAINSTORMING HOURS:_____   RESEARCH HOURS:_____
EDITING HOURS:_____   READING HOURS:_____

DAILY ACCOMPLISHMENTS   **SATURDAY 16**

WORD COUNT:_____   MARKETING HOURS:_____
BRAINSTORMING HOURS:_____   RESEARCH HOURS:_____
EDITING HOURS:_____   READING HOURS:_____

DAILY ACCOMPLISHMENTS   **SUNDAY 17**

WORD COUNT:_____   MARKETING HOURS:_____
BRAINSTORMING HOURS:_____   RESEARCH HOURS:_____
EDITING HOURS:_____   READING HOURS:_____

DAILY ACCOMPLISHMENTS   **MONDAY 18**

WORD COUNT:_____   MARKETING HOURS:_____
BRAINSTORMING HOURS:_____   RESEARCH HOURS:_____
EDITING HOURS:_____   READING HOURS:_____

DAILY ACCOMPLISHMENTS   **TUESDAY 19**

WORD COUNT:_____   MARKETING HOURS:_____
BRAINSTORMING HOURS:_____   RESEARCH HOURS:_____
EDITING HOURS:_____   READING HOURS:_____

DAILY ACCOMPLISHMENTS   **WEDNESDAY 20**

WORD COUNT:_____   MARKETING HOURS:_____
BRAINSTORMING HOURS:_____   RESEARCH HOURS:_____
EDITING HOURS:_____   READING HOURS:_____

DAILY ACCOMPLISHMENTS   **THURSDAY 21**

WORD COUNT:_____   MARKETING HOURS:_____
BRAINSTORMING HOURS:_____   RESEARCH HOURS:_____
EDITING HOURS:_____   READING HOURS:_____

WEEKLY OVERVIEW

EXERCISE: Take 5-minute to write something with the 2 words below:

TV   Post-it

Post your exercise on the 4HP Accountable Authors Group on Facebook!

What was your sprint time and top word count?

_____

List a new song you discovered this week:

_____

Favorite food or drink this week:

_____

How did you reward yourself?

_____

What project(s) did you work on?

_____

What are you reading?

_____

What went well this week?

_____

What could improve this week?

_____

_____

_____

TOTAL FOR THE WEEK

Word Count:_____   Marketing Hours:_____
Brainstorming Hours:_____   Research Hours:_____
Editing Hours:_____   Reading Hours:_____

Don't forget to color in your grid!

The Cheerleader

"Just keep swimming!"

~ Dory (Finding Nemo)

THE ARCHITECT

Don't edit as you write. It will only slow down the drafting process. Worry about that later.

THE RESEARCHER

Check your story for unnecessary characters. It seems weird, but remember, Joseph Stalin would have photos retouched to remove people who were no longer in office or died. Is there a character who don't support your plot or main characters?
Try taking them out!

THE TASKMASTER

Believe in yourself. Decide you are a great writer--and that's exactly what you will be.

OCTOBER

WEEK 4

DAILY ACCOMPLISHMENTS   **FRIDAY 22**

WORD COUNT:_____
BRAINSTORMING HOURS:_____
EDITING HOURS:_____

MARKETING HOURS:_____
RESEARCH HOURS:_____
READING HOURS:_____

DAILY ACCOMPLISHMENTS   **SATURDAY 23**

WORD COUNT:_____
BRAINSTORMING HOURS:_____
EDITING HOURS:_____

MARKETING HOURS:_____
RESEARCH HOURS:_____
READING HOURS:_____

DAILY ACCOMPLISHMENTS   **SUNDAY 24**

WORD COUNT:_____
BRAINSTORMING HOURS:_____
EDITING HOURS:_____

MARKETING HOURS:_____
RESEARCH HOURS:_____
READING HOURS:_____

DAILY ACCOMPLISHMENTS   **MONDAY 25**

WORD COUNT:_____
BRAINSTORMING HOURS:_____
EDITING HOURS:_____

MARKETING HOURS:_____
RESEARCH HOURS:_____
READING HOURS:_____

DAILY ACCOMPLISHMENTS   **TUESDAY 26**

WORD COUNT:_____
BRAINSTORMING HOURS:_____
EDITING HOURS:_____

MARKETING HOURS:_____
RESEARCH HOURS:_____
READING HOURS:_____

DAILY ACCOMPLISHMENTS   **WEDNESDAY 27**

WORD COUNT:_____
BRAINSTORMING HOURS:_____
EDITING HOURS:_____

MARKETING HOURS:_____
RESEARCH HOURS:_____
READING HOURS:_____

DAILY ACCOMPLISHMENTS   **THURSDAY 28**

WORD COUNT:_____
BRAINSTORMING HOURS:_____
EDITING HOURS:_____

MARKETING HOURS:_____
RESEARCH HOURS:_____
READING HOURS:_____

OCTOBER

WEEKLY OVERVIEW

EXERCISE: Take 5-minute to write something with the 2 words below:

Warm   Ice

Post your exercise on the 4HP Accountable Authors Group on Facebook!

What was your sprint time and top word count?

_____

List a new song you discovered this week:

_____

Favorite food or drink this week:

_____

How did you reward yourself?

_____

What project(s) did you work on?

_____

What are you reading?

_____

What went well this week?

_____

What could improve this week?

_____

_____

_____

TOTAL FOR THE WEEK

Word Count:_____   Marketing Hours:_____
Brainstorming Hours:_____   Research Hours:_____
Editing Hours:_____   Reading Hours:_____

Don't forget to color in your grid!

The Cheerleader

Songs are filled with helpful advice.
Write down an inspiring quote here.

THE ARCHITECT

Write under different circumstances
once this week (*music, background,
process, etc. Shake it up
somehow!*).
How did it go?

OCTOBER

THE RESEARCHER

Are you telling the right character's story? Try flipping it out and write a scene from a different character's point-of-view! For example, telling a story from the POV of a shark, the diver, or even the boat can differ drastically!

THE TASKMASTER

Stop wasting time on social media or watching Netflix. Get back to the part where you are creating worlds.

OCTOBER

213

DAILY ACCOMPLISHMENTS   **FRIDAY 29**

WORD COUNT:_____   MARKETING HOURS:_____
BRAINSTORMING HOURS:_____   RESEARCH HOURS:_____
EDITING HOURS:_____   READING HOURS:_____

DAILY ACCOMPLISHMENTS   **SATURDAY 30**

WORD COUNT:_____   MARKETING HOURS:_____
BRAINSTORMING HOURS:_____   RESEARCH HOURS:_____
EDITING HOURS:_____   READING HOURS:_____

DAILY ACCOMPLISHMENTS   **SUNDAY 31**

WORD COUNT:_____   MARKETING HOURS:_____
BRAINSTORMING HOURS:_____   RESEARCH HOURS:_____
EDITING HOURS:_____   READING HOURS:_____

THE RESEARCHER

Quick! List all the signs of being undead (*whether your own symptoms or asking for friend*)!
Are these signs of a vampire bite or zombie infection?

OCTOBER

214

WEEKLY OVERVIEW

EXERCISE: Take 5-minute to write something with the 2 words below:

Vampire   Zombie

Post your exercise on the 4HP Accountable Authors Group on Facebook!

What was your sprint time and top word count?

_____

List a new song you discovered this week:

_____

Favorite food or drink this week:

_____

How did you reward yourself?

_____

What project(s) did you work on?

_____

What are you reading?

_____

What went well this week?

_____

What could improve this week?

_____

_____

_____

TOTAL FOR THE WEEK

Word Count:_____   Marketing Hours:_____
Brainstorming Hours:_____   Research Hours:_____
Editing Hours:_____   Reading Hours:_____

Don't forget to color in your grid!

MONTHLY ACTIVITY GRID

WRITING OR WORD COUNT	
BRAINSTORMING	
EDITING	
MARKETING OR SOCIAL MEDIA	
RESEARCH	
READING	
OTHER:	

OCTOBER

YOUR AVERAGE WORD COUNT FOR THE MONTH

Total Word Count:_____ Divided by _____ days =_____

TOTAL FOR THE YEAR SO FAR

Word Count:_____   Marketing Hours:_____
Brainstorming Hours:_____   Research Hours:_____
Editing Hours:_____   Reading Hours:_____

JOURNAL

What was your **top week**?

_____

What made your **top week** successful?

_____

What was your biggest **obstacle**?

_____

How did you **overcome** this? Or could do better next time?

_____

_____

What was your biggest **achievement**?

_____

_____

What **inspired** you most this month?

_____

Did you **discover** a new writing tip or advice this month?

_____

_____

TOTAL FOR THE MONTH

Word Count:_____   Research Hours:_____
Brainstorming Hours:_____   Reading Hours:_____
Editing Hours:_____
Marketing Hours:_____

TOTAL FOR THE YEAR SO FAR

Word Count:_____   Research Hours:_____
Brainstorming Hours:_____   Reading Hours:_____
Editing Hours:_____
Marketing Hours:_____

Don't forget to color in your grid!

NOVEMBER

"NATIONAL NOVEL WRITING MONTH! Sign up to participate in this international celebration, here: nanowrimo.org . Writing a novel alone can be difficult, but NaNoWriMo helps you track progress, set milestones, connect with a vast writers community, and participate in events designed to make sure you finish your novel. Oh, and best of all, it's free!

Nov 1 - Saint's Day

Nov 11 - Veteran's Day
Nov. 25 - Thanksgiving

Nov 26 - Black Friday

WHAT DOES YOUR MONTH LOOK LIKE

Holidays:_____   Weekends:_____

Weekdays:_____   Other:_____

What **project(s)** do you plan on working on?

_____

What **goal** are you aiming to achieve?

_____

What will be your biggest **obstacle** this month?

_____

How will you **overcome** this? Or adjust for this?

_____

What will be your End of the Month **reward**?

_____

GOALS FOR THIS MONTH

Word Count:_____   Marketing Hours:_____

Brainstorming Hours:_____   Research Hours:_____

Editing Hours:_____   Reading Hours:_____

Week 1

DAILY ACCOMPLISHMENTS	**MONDAY 1**

*Word Count:*_____   *Marketing Hours:*_____

*Brainstorming Hours:*_____   *Research Hours:*_____

*Editing Hours:*_____   *Reading Hours:*_____

DAILY ACCOMPLISHMENTS	**TUESDAY 2**

*Word Count:*_____   *Marketing Hours:*_____

*Brainstorming Hours:*_____   *Research Hours:*_____

*Editing Hours:*_____   *Reading Hours:*_____

DAILY ACCOMPLISHMENTS	**WEDNESDAY 3**

*Word Count:*_____   *Marketing Hours:*_____

*Brainstorming Hours:*_____   *Research Hours:*_____

*Editing Hours:*_____   *Reading Hours:*_____

DAILY ACCOMPLISHMENTS	**THURSDAY 4**

*Word Count:*_____   *Marketing Hours:*_____

*Brainstorming Hours:*_____   *Research Hours:*_____

*Editing Hours:*_____   *Reading Hours:*_____

DAILY ACCOMPLISHMENTS	**FRIDAY 5**

*Word Count:*_____   *Marketing Hours:*_____

*Brainstorming Hours:*_____   *Research Hours:*_____

*Editing Hours:*_____   *Reading Hours:*_____

DAILY ACCOMPLISHMENTS	**SATURDAY 6**

*Word Count:*_____   *Marketing Hours:*_____

*Brainstorming Hours:*_____   *Research Hours:*_____

*Editing Hours:*_____   *Reading Hours:*_____

DAILY ACCOMPLISHMENTS	**SUNDAY 7**

*Word Count:*_____   *Marketing Hours:*_____

*Brainstorming Hours:*_____   *Research Hours:*_____

*Editing Hours:*_____   *Reading Hours:*_____

WEEKLY OVERVIEW

EXERCISE: Take 5-minute to write something with the 2 words below:

Rose   Muffin

Post your exercise on the 4HP Accountable Authors Group on Facebook!

What was your sprint time and top word count?

_____

List a new song you discovered this week:

_____

Favorite food or drink this week:

_____

How did you reward yourself?

_____

What project(s) did you work on?

_____

What are you reading?

_____

What went well this week?

_____

What could improve this week?

_____

_____

_____

TOTAL FOR THE WEEK

Word Count:_____   Marketing Hours:_____
Brainstorming Hours:_____   Research Hours:_____
Editing Hours:_____   Reading Hours:_____

Don't forget to color in your grid!

The Cheerleader

Post the cover (*or mock cover*) of your current project on the 4HP Accountable Authors group on Facebook.

THE ARCHITECT

"If you wait for inspiration to write, you're not a writer; you're a waiter."

~ *Dan Poyner*

THE RESEARCHER

What's the best fictional death you've read in a story? What made this so epic? What was the worst death? Why? What lessons from these impressions can you apply to your writing?

THE TASKMASTER

Ctrl Find "shrug," "nod," "sigh," and any other words you use too frequently and clean that crap up!

Week 2

DAILY ACCOMPLISHMENTS   **MONDAY 8**

*WORD COUNT:*_____   *MARKETING HOURS:*_____
*BRAINSTORMING HOURS:*_____ *RESEARCH HOURS:*_____
*EDITING HOURS:*_____   *READING HOURS:*_____

DAILY ACCOMPLISHMENTS   **TUESDAY 9**

*WORD COUNT:*_____   *MARKETING HOURS:*_____
*BRAINSTORMING HOURS:*_____ *RESEARCH HOURS:*_____
*EDITING HOURS:*_____   *READING HOURS:*_____

DAILY ACCOMPLISHMENTS   **WEDNESDAY 10**

*WORD COUNT:*_____   *MARKETING HOURS:*_____
*BRAINSTORMING HOURS:*_____ *RESEARCH HOURS:*_____
*EDITING HOURS:*_____   *READING HOURS:*_____

DAILY ACCOMPLISHMENTS   **THURSDAY 11**

*WORD COUNT:*_____   *MARKETING HOURS:*_____
*BRAINSTORMING HOURS:*_____ *RESEARCH HOURS:*_____
*EDITING HOURS:*_____   *READING HOURS:*_____

DAILY ACCOMPLISHMENTS   **FRIDAY 12**

*WORD COUNT:*_____   *MARKETING HOURS:*_____
*BRAINSTORMING HOURS:*_____ *RESEARCH HOURS:*_____
*EDITING HOURS:*_____   *READING HOURS:*_____

DAILY ACCOMPLISHMENTS   **SATURDAY 13**

*WORD COUNT:*_____   *MARKETING HOURS:*_____
*BRAINSTORMING HOURS:*_____ *RESEARCH HOURS:*_____
*EDITING HOURS:*_____   *READING HOURS:*_____

DAILY ACCOMPLISHMENTS   **SUNDAY 14**

*WORD COUNT:*_____   *MARKETING HOURS:*_____
*BRAINSTORMING HOURS:*_____ *RESEARCH HOURS:*_____
*EDITING HOURS:*_____   *READING HOURS:*_____

WEEKLY OVERVIEW

EXERCISE: Take 5-minute to write something with the 2 words below:

Coffee   Tile

Post your exercise on the 4HP Accountable Authors Group on Facebook!

What was your sprint time and top word count?

_____

List a new song you discovered this week:

_____

Favorite food or drink this week:

_____

How did you reward yourself?

_____

What project(s) did you work on?

_____

What are you reading?

_____

What went well this week?

_____

What could improve this week?

_____

_____

_____

TOTAL FOR THE WEEK

Word Count:_____   Marketing Hours:_____
Brainstorming Hours:_____   Research Hours:_____
Editing Hours:_____   Reading Hours:_____

Don't forget to color in your grid!

The Cheerleader

"Life will only change when you become more committed to your dreams than you are to your comfort zone."

~ Billy Cox

THE ARCHITECT

Swap a chapter or short story with a critique partner and edit. What do you like about their style? Where can they improve? How is your writing different?

THE RESEARCHER

My hat goes off to crime, mystery, and horror writers. They kill people--creatively! But real life can be even more surprising. Here's a strange one: US President Zachary Taylor passed from eating too many cherries while drinking milk... at a 4th of July Party after only serving 16 months in office.

THE TASKMASTER

You are expected to fail. We will all fail several times in our lives. It's what you do with that failure that makes all the difference. Learn from it.

Week 3

NOVEMBER

DAILY ACCOMPLISHMENTS	**MONDAY 15**
Word Count:_____	Marketing Hours:_____
Brainstorming Hours:_____	Research Hours:_____
Editing Hours:_____	Reading Hours:_____

DAILY ACCOMPLISHMENTS	**TUESDAY 16**
Word Count:_____	Marketing Hours:_____
Brainstorming Hours:_____	Research Hours:_____
Editing Hours:_____	Reading Hours:_____

DAILY ACCOMPLISHMENTS	**WEDNESDAY 17**
Word Count:_____	Marketing Hours:_____
Brainstorming Hours:_____	Research Hours:_____
Editing Hours:_____	Reading Hours:_____

DAILY ACCOMPLISHMENTS	**THURSDAY 18**
Word Count:_____	Marketing Hours:_____
Brainstorming Hours:_____	Research Hours:_____
Editing Hours:_____	Reading Hours:_____

DAILY ACCOMPLISHMENTS	**FRIDAY 19**
Word Count:_____	Marketing Hours:_____
Brainstorming Hours:_____	Research Hours:_____
Editing Hours:_____	Reading Hours:_____

DAILY ACCOMPLISHMENTS	**SATURDAY 20**
Word Count:_____	Marketing Hours:_____
Brainstorming Hours:_____	Research Hours:_____
Editing Hours:_____	Reading Hours:_____

DAILY ACCOMPLISHMENTS	**SUNDAY 21**
Word Count:_____	Marketing Hours:_____
Brainstorming Hours:_____	Research Hours:_____
Editing Hours:_____	Reading Hours:_____

WEEKLY OVERVIEW

EXERCISE: Take 5-minute to write something with the 2 words below:

Movement   Song

Post your exercise on the 4HP Accountable Authors Group on Facebook!

What was your sprint time and top word count?

_____

List a new song you discovered this week:

_____

Favorite food or drink this week:

_____

How did you reward yourself?

_____

What project(s) did you work on?

_____

What are you reading?

_____

What went well this week?

_____

What could improve this week?

_____

_____

_____

TOTAL FOR THE WEEK

Word Count:_____   Marketing Hours:_____
Brainstorming Hours:_____   Research Hours:_____
Editing Hours:_____   Reading Hours:_____

Don't forget to color in your grid!

The Cheerleader

Treat yourself this week! Meet up with writers at a cafe or online for an hour long writing session.

THE ARCHITECT

"I write to give myself strength. I write to be the characters that I am not. I write to explore all the things I'm afraid of."

~ Joss Whedon

THE RESEARCHER

Pets add agency: horses, dogs, cats, and even talking parrots. Andrew Jackson had a parrot named Polly--who cursed like a sailor to the point they removed her from his funeral!

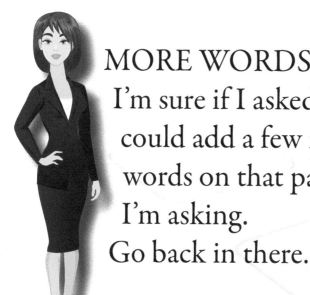

THE TASKMASTER

MORE WORDS!!!
I'm sure if I asked, you could add a few more words on that page.
I'm asking.
Go back in there.

NOVEMBER

WEEK 4

DAILY ACCOMPLISHMENTS	**MONDAY 22**
*WORD COUNT:*_____	*MARKETING HOURS:*_____
*BRAINSTORMING HOURS:*_____	*RESEARCH HOURS:*_____
*EDITING HOURS:*_____	*READING HOURS:*_____

DAILY ACCOMPLISHMENTS	**TUESDAY 23**
*WORD COUNT:*_____	*MARKETING HOURS:*_____
*BRAINSTORMING HOURS:*_____	*RESEARCH HOURS:*_____
*EDITING HOURS:*_____	*READING HOURS:*_____

DAILY ACCOMPLISHMENTS	**WEDNESDAY 24**
*WORD COUNT:*_____	*MARKETING HOURS:*_____
*BRAINSTORMING HOURS:*_____	*RESEARCH HOURS:*_____
*EDITING HOURS:*_____	*READING HOURS:*_____

DAILY ACCOMPLISHMENTS	**THURSDAY 25**
*WORD COUNT:*_____	*MARKETING HOURS:*_____
*BRAINSTORMING HOURS:*_____	*RESEARCH HOURS:*_____
*EDITING HOURS:*_____	*READING HOURS:*_____

DAILY ACCOMPLISHMENTS	**FRIDAY 26**
*WORD COUNT:*_____	*MARKETING HOURS:*_____
*BRAINSTORMING HOURS:*_____	*RESEARCH HOURS:*_____
*EDITING HOURS:*_____	*READING HOURS:*_____

DAILY ACCOMPLISHMENTS	**SATURDAY 27**
*WORD COUNT:*_____	*MARKETING HOURS:*_____
*BRAINSTORMING HOURS:*_____	*RESEARCH HOURS:*_____
*EDITING HOURS:*_____	*READING HOURS:*_____

DAILY ACCOMPLISHMENTS	**SUNDAY 28**
*WORD COUNT:*_____	*MARKETING HOURS:*_____
*BRAINSTORMING HOURS:*_____	*RESEARCH HOURS:*_____
*EDITING HOURS:*_____	*READING HOURS:*_____

NOVEMBER

WEEKLY OVERVIEW

EXERCISE: Take 5-minute to write something with the 2 words below:

Repeat   Flaw

Post your exercise on the 4HP Accountable Authors Group on Facebook!

What was your sprint time and top word count?

_____

List a new song you discovered this week:

_____

Favorite food or drink this week:

_____

How did you reward yourself?

_____

What project(s) did you work on?

_____

What are you reading?

_____

What went well this week?

_____

What could improve this week?

_____

_____

TOTAL FOR THE WEEK

Word Count:_____   Marketing Hours:_____
Brainstorming Hours:_____   Research Hours:_____
Editing Hours:_____   Reading Hours:_____

Don't forget to color in your grid!

The Cheerleader

"The way that I write a novel is not going to be the way that you write a novel. Only you know how you can do it, and you've got to figure it out for yourself."

~ Sarah Dessen

THE ARCHITECT

Big Picture Time: What kind of project-wide issues are you facing right now? Think about how you can address these moving forward.

THE RESEARCHER

Follow two other writers on social media who are participating in Nanowrimo. If they can do it, so can you!

THE TASKMASTER

Have you been practicing your elevator pitch for your book? Do it some more, and polish it, even if it is not finished yet. You need to be able to say it in your sleep.

NOVEMBER

DAILY ACCOMPLISHMENTS		**MONDAY 29**
WORD COUNT:	*MARKETING HOURS:*	
BRAINSTORMING HOURS:	*RESEARCH HOURS:*	
EDITING HOURS:	*READING HOURS:*	

DAILY ACCOMPLISHMENTS		**TUESDAY 30**
WORD COUNT:	*MARKETING HOURS:*	
BRAINSTORMING HOURS:	*RESEARCH HOURS:*	
EDITING HOURS:	*READING HOURS:*	

The Cheerleader

"This sentence has five words. Here are five more words. Five-word sentences are fine. But several together become monotonous. Listen to what is happening. The writing is getting boring. The sound of it drones. It's like a stuck record. The ear demands some variety. Now listen. I vary the sentence length, and I create music. Music. The writing sings. It has a pleasant rhythm, a lilt, a harmony. I use short sentences. And I use sentences of medium length. And sometimes, when I am certain the reader is rested, I will engage him with a sentence of considerable length, a sentence that burns with energy and builds with all the impetus of a crescendo, the roll of the drums, the crash of the cymbals—sounds that say listen to this, it is important."

~ Gary Provost

Weekly Overview

EXERCISE: Take 5-minute to write something with the 2 words below:

Author   Journey

Post your exercise on the 4HP Accountable Authors Group on Facebook!

What was your sprint time and top word count?

_____

List a new song you discovered this week:

_____

Favorite food or drink this week:

_____

How did you reward yourself?

_____

What project(s) did you work on?

_____

What are you reading?

_____

What went well this week?

_____

What could improve this week?

_____

_____

_____

TOTAL FOR THE WEEK

Word Count:_____   Marketing Hours:_____
Brainstorming Hours:_____   Research Hours:_____
Editing Hours:_____   Reading Hours:_____

Don't forget to color in your grid!

MONTHLY ACTIVITY GRID

WRITING OR WORD COUNT	
BRAINSTORMING	
EDITING	
MARKETING OR SOCIAL MEDIA	
RESEARCH	
READING	
OTHER:	

YOUR AVERAGE WORD COUNT FOR THE MONTH

Total Word Count:_____ Divided by _____ days =_____

TOTAL FOR THE YEAR SO FAR

Word Count:_____   Marketing Hours:_____
Brainstorming Hours:_____   Research Hours:_____
Editing Hours:_____   Reading Hours:_____

JOURNAL

What was your **top week**?

_____

What made your **top week** successful?

_____

What was your biggest **obstacle**?

_____

How did you **overcome** this? Or could do better next time?

_____

_____

What was your biggest **achievement**?

_____

_____

What **inspired** you most this month?

_____

Did you **discover** a new writing tip or advice this month?

_____

_____

TOTAL FOR THE MONTH

Word Count:_____   Marketing Hours:_____
Brainstorming Hours:_____   Research Hours:_____
Editing Hours:_____   Reading Hours:_____

TOTAL FOR THE YEAR SO FAR

Word Count:_____   Marketing Hours:_____
Brainstorming Hours:_____   Research Hours:_____
Editing Hours:_____   Reading Hours:_____

Don't forget to color in your grid!

DECEMBER

O kay. Breathe. You surived NANO (if you participated). We are in the home stretch. You need to double your efforts, review your goal for the month (and year), and make sure you cross that finish line. This month is filled with distractions like food-filled holidays. Make sure you plan your productive and enjoyment time equally.

Dec 24 - Christmas Eve   *Dec. 25 - Christmas*   *Dec. 31 - New Year's Eve*

WHAT DOES YOUR MONTH LOOK LIKE

Holidays:_____   Weekends:_____
Weekdays:_____   Other:_____

What **project(s)** do you plan on working on?

_____

What **goal** are you aiming to achieve?

_____

What will be your biggest **obstacle** this month?

_____

How will you **overcome** this? Or adjust for this?

_____

What will be your End of the Month **reward**?

_____

GOALS FOR THIS MONTH

Word Count:_____   Marketing Hours:_____
Brainstorming Hours:_____   Research Hours:_____
Editing Hours:_____   Reading Hours:_____

241

WEEK 1

DAILY ACCOMPLISHMENTS	**WEDNESDAY 1**
WORD COUNT:	*MARKETING HOURS:*
BRAINSTORMING HOURS:	*RESEARCH HOURS:*
EDITING HOURS:	*READING HOURS:*

DAILY ACCOMPLISHMENTS	**THURSDAY 2**
WORD COUNT:	*MARKETING HOURS:*
BRAINSTORMING HOURS:	*RESEARCH HOURS:*
EDITING HOURS:	*READING HOURS:*

DAILY ACCOMPLISHMENTS	**FRIDAY 3**
WORD COUNT:	*MARKETING HOURS:*
BRAINSTORMING HOURS:	*RESEARCH HOURS:*
EDITING HOURS:	*READING HOURS:*

DAILY ACCOMPLISHMENTS	**SATURDAY 4**
WORD COUNT:	*MARKETING HOURS:*
BRAINSTORMING HOURS:	*RESEARCH HOURS:*
EDITING HOURS:	*READING HOURS:*

DAILY ACCOMPLISHMENTS	**SUNDAY 5**
WORD COUNT:	*MARKETING HOURS:*
BRAINSTORMING HOURS:	*RESEARCH HOURS:*
EDITING HOURS:	*READING HOURS:*

DAILY ACCOMPLISHMENTS	**MONDAY 6**
WORD COUNT:	*MARKETING HOURS:*
BRAINSTORMING HOURS:	*RESEARCH HOURS:*
EDITING HOURS:	*READING HOURS:*

DAILY ACCOMPLISHMENTS	**TUESDAY 7**
WORD COUNT:	*MARKETING HOURS:*
BRAINSTORMING HOURS:	*RESEARCH HOURS:*
EDITING HOURS:	*READING HOURS:*

WEEKLY OVERVIEW

EXERCISE: Take 5-minute to write something with the 2 words below:

Box   Cheese

Post your exercise on the 4HP Accountable Authors Group on Facebook!

What was your sprint time and top word count?

_____

List a new song you discovered this week:

_____

Favorite food or drink this week:

_____

How did you reward yourself?

_____

What project(s) did you work on?

_____

What are you reading?

_____

What went well this week?

_____

What could improve this week?

_____

_____

TOTAL FOR THE WEEK

Word Count:_____   Marketing Hours:_____
Brainstorming Hours:_____   Research Hours:_____
Editing Hours:_____   Reading Hours:_____

Don't forget to color in your grid!

The Cheerleader

The Doctor Is In: What struggles are your characters facing right now? Work through the issues here.

THE ARCHITECT

"There is nothing to writing. All you do is sit down at the typewriter and bleed."

~ Ernest Hemingway

THE RESEARCHER

Weapons--let those guns and swords cause trouble in the plot and world. It amazes me how long a well-made blade can last. The ancient Sword of Goujian was discovered in Hubei, China after spending two millennia in a tomb. It's still razor sharp!

THE TASKMASTER

Editors are your friends. They are not your nice friends. They can be downright mean sometimes. They are simply making your work better. Remember that.

DECEMBER

DAILY ACCOMPLISHMENTS   **WEDNESDAY 8**

*Word Count:*_____   *Marketing Hours:*_____
*Brainstorming Hours:*_____   *Research Hours:*_____
*Editing Hours:*_____   *Reading Hours:*_____

DAILY ACCOMPLISHMENTS   **THURSDAY 9**

*Word Count:*_____   *Marketing Hours:*_____
*Brainstorming Hours:*_____   *Research Hours:*_____
*Editing Hours:*_____   *Reading Hours:*_____

DAILY ACCOMPLISHMENTS   **FRIDAY 10**

*Word Count:*_____   *Marketing Hours:*_____
*Brainstorming Hours:*_____   *Research Hours:*_____
*Editing Hours:*_____   *Reading Hours:*_____

DAILY ACCOMPLISHMENTS   **SATURDAY 11**

*Word Count:*_____   *Marketing Hours:*_____
*Brainstorming Hours:*_____   *Research Hours:*_____
*Editing Hours:*_____   *Reading Hours:*_____

DAILY ACCOMPLISHMENTS   **SUNDAY 12**

*Word Count:*_____   *Marketing Hours:*_____
*Brainstorming Hours:*_____   *Research Hours:*_____
*Editing Hours:*_____   *Reading Hours:*_____

DAILY ACCOMPLISHMENTS   **MONDAY 13**

*Word Count:*_____   *Marketing Hours:*_____
*Brainstorming Hours:*_____   *Research Hours:*_____
*Editing Hours:*_____   *Reading Hours:*_____

DAILY ACCOMPLISHMENTS   **TUESDAY 14**

*Word Count:*_____   *Marketing Hours:*_____
*Brainstorming Hours:*_____   *Research Hours:*_____
*Editing Hours:*_____   *Reading Hours:*_____

DECEMBER

WEEKLY OVERVIEW

EXERCISE: Take 5-minute to write something with the 2 words below:

Blue   Panda

Post your exercise on the 4HP Accountable Authors Group on Facebook!

What was your sprint time and top word count?

_____

List a new song you discovered this week:

_____

Favorite food or drink this week:

_____

How did you reward yourself?

_____

What project(s) did you work on?

_____

What are you reading?

_____

What went well this week?

_____

What could improve this week?

_____

_____

_____

TOTAL FOR THE WEEK

Word Count:_____　　Marketing Hours:_____
Brainstorming Hours:_____　Research Hours:_____
Editing Hours:_____　Reading Hours:_____

Don't forget to color in your grid!

The Cheerleader

"*I've never felt such tension. It's like riding a psychotic horse toward a burning stable.*"

~ Armand Goldman

THE ARCHITECT

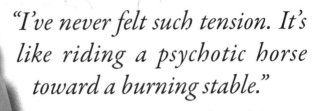

If you want your scene to come alive for the reader, try using all of your senses:

smell, sound, touch, taste, and sight.

THE RESEARCHER

Writing on the beach or in a cabin in the woods? Pros/Cons.

THE TASKMASTER

Hero to Zero. Start each day with a goal. When you achieve it, celebrate for a moment, then start again.

WEEK 3

DAILY ACCOMPLISHMENTS   **WEDNESDAY 15**

WORD COUNT:_____   MARKETING HOURS:_____
BRAINSTORMING HOURS:_____   RESEARCH HOURS:_____
EDITING HOURS:_____   READING HOURS:_____

DAILY ACCOMPLISHMENTS   **THURSDAY 16**

WORD COUNT:_____   MARKETING HOURS:_____
BRAINSTORMING HOURS:_____   RESEARCH HOURS:_____
EDITING HOURS:_____   READING HOURS:_____

DAILY ACCOMPLISHMENTS   **FRIDAY 17**

WORD COUNT:_____   MARKETING HOURS:_____
BRAINSTORMING HOURS:_____   RESEARCH HOURS:_____
EDITING HOURS:_____   READING HOURS:_____

DAILY ACCOMPLISHMENTS   **SATURDAY 18**

WORD COUNT:_____   MARKETING HOURS:_____
BRAINSTORMING HOURS:_____   RESEARCH HOURS:_____
EDITING HOURS:_____   READING HOURS:_____

DAILY ACCOMPLISHMENTS   **SUNDAY 19**

WORD COUNT:_____   MARKETING HOURS:_____
BRAINSTORMING HOURS:_____   RESEARCH HOURS:_____
EDITING HOURS:_____   READING HOURS:_____

DAILY ACCOMPLISHMENTS   **MONDAY 20**

WORD COUNT:_____   MARKETING HOURS:_____
BRAINSTORMING HOURS:_____   RESEARCH HOURS:_____
EDITING HOURS:_____   READING HOURS:_____

DAILY ACCOMPLISHMENTS   **TUESDAY 21**

WORD COUNT:_____   MARKETING HOURS:_____
BRAINSTORMING HOURS:_____   RESEARCH HOURS:_____
EDITING HOURS:_____   READING HOURS:_____

Weekly Overview

EXERCISE: Take 5-minute to write something with the 2 words below:

Weird   Planner

Post your exercise on the 4HP Accountable Authors Group on Facebook!

What was your sprint time and top word count?

_____

List a new song you discovered this week:

_____

Favorite food or drink this week:

_____

How did you reward yourself?

_____

What project(s) did you work on?

_____

What are you reading?

_____

What went well this week?

_____

What could improve this week?

_____

_____

_____

TOTAL FOR THE WEEK

Word Count:_____   Marketing Hours:_____
Brainstorming Hours:_____   Research Hours:_____
Editing Hours:_____   Reading Hours:_____

Don't forget to color in your grid!

The Cheerleader

Follow two other writers on social media who are participating in Nanowrimo. If they can do it, so can you!

THE ARCHITECT

"Writing seems to be the only job where what you think and feel really matters."
~ Richard North Patterson

THE RESEARCHER

A blind man once crossed a 140 km salt flat desert with only a GPS to guide him. If he can do that, I am pretty sure you can achieve your goals as a writer!

THE TASKMASTER

Don't let anyone tell you that your work isn't amazing. They aren't your audience. Ignore the haters. (*Haters gonna hate.*)

Daily Accomplishments   **Wednesday 22**

*Word Count:*_____   *Marketing Hours:*_____
*Brainstorming Hours:*_____   *Research Hours:*_____
*Editing Hours:*_____   *Reading Hours:*_____

Daily Accomplishments   **Thursday 23**

*Word Count:*_____   *Marketing Hours:*_____
*Brainstorming Hours:*_____   *Research Hours:*_____
*Editing Hours:*_____   *Reading Hours:*_____

Daily Accomplishments   **Friday 24**

*Word Count:*_____   *Marketing Hours:*_____
*Brainstorming Hours:*_____   *Research Hours:*_____
*Editing Hours:*_____   *Reading Hours:*_____

Daily Accomplishments   **Saturday 25**

*Word Count:*_____   *Marketing Hours:*_____
*Brainstorming Hours:*_____   *Research Hours:*_____
*Editing Hours:*_____   *Reading Hours:*_____

Daily Accomplishments   **Sunday 26**

*Word Count:*_____   *Marketing Hours:*_____
*Brainstorming Hours:*_____   *Research Hours:*_____
*Editing Hours:*_____   *Reading Hours:*_____

Daily Accomplishments   **Monday 27**

*Word Count:*_____   *Marketing Hours:*_____
*Brainstorming Hours:*_____   *Research Hours:*_____
*Editing Hours:*_____   *Reading Hours:*_____

Daily Accomplishments   **Tuesday 28**

*Word Count:*_____   *Marketing Hours:*_____
*Brainstorming Hours:*_____   *Research Hours:*_____
*Editing Hours:*_____   *Reading Hours:*_____

DECEMBER

WEEKLY OVERVIEW

EXERCISE: Take 5-minute to write something with the 2 words below:

Week   Mustache

Post your exercise on the 4HP Accountable Authors Group on Facebook!

What was your sprint time and top word count?

_____

List a new song you discovered this week:

_____

Favorite food or drink this week:

_____

How did you reward yourself?

_____

What project(s) did you work on?

_____

What are you reading?

_____

What went well this week?

_____

What could improve this week?

_____

_____

_____

TOTAL FOR THE WEEK

Word Count:_____   Marketing Hours:_____
Brainstorming Hours:_____   Research Hours:_____
Editing Hours:_____   Reading Hours:_____

Don't forget to color in your grid!

The Cheerleader

"This is how you do it: you sit down at a keyboard and you put one word after another until it is done. It's that easy, and that hard."

~ Neil Gaiman

THE ARCHITECT

Reflect on your NanoWrimo experience: How was it this year? What worked for you? What should you avoid next time?

THE RESEARCHER

Declare a focus and double down on one project. Don't be like Napoleon. He was attacked by over 3,000 rabbits during a hunt when they turned and came after him and his men!

THE TASKMASTER

You are almost there...
GO GO GO GO!
You've got this!

DAILY ACCOMPLISHMENTS	**WEDNESDAY 29**
Word Count:	*Marketing Hours:*
Brainstorming Hours:	*Research Hours:*
Editing Hours:	*Reading Hours:*

DAILY ACCOMPLISHMENTS	**THURSDAY 30**
Word Count:	*Marketing Hours:*
Brainstorming Hours:	*Research Hours:*
Editing Hours:	*Reading Hours:*

DAILY ACCOMPLISHMENTS	**FRIDAY 31**
Word Count:	*Marketing Hours:*
Brainstorming Hours:	*Research Hours:*
Editing Hours:	*Reading Hours:*

THE ARCHITECT

How would you describe your writing style? Pantser, Plotter, or Plantser?

I hope you consider yourself a badass! I know I do. YOU DID IT! You made it to the end of this book. Now grab next year's version and start again.

WEEKLY OVERVIEW

EXERCISE: Take 5-minute to write something with the 2 words below:

Sheet   Terror

Post your exercise on the 4HP Accountable Authors Group on Facebook!

What was your sprint time and top word count?

_____

List a new song you discovered this week:

_____

Favorite food or drink this week:

_____

How did you reward yourself?

_____

What project(s) did you work on?

_____

What are you reading?

_____

What went well this week?

_____

What could improve this week?

_____

_____

_____

TOTAL FOR THE WEEK

Word Count:_____   Marketing Hours:_____
Brainstorming Hours:_____   Research Hours:_____
Editing Hours:_____   Reading Hours:_____

Don't forget to color in your grid!

MONTHLY ACTIVITY GRID

DECEMBER

WRITING OR WORD COUNT	1 2 3 4 5 6 7 8 9 10 11 12 13 14 15 16 17 18 19 20 21 22 23 24 25 26 27 28 29 30 31
BRAINSTORMING	
EDITING	
MARKETING OR SOCIAL MEDIA	
RESEARCH	
READING	
OTHER:	

YOUR AVERAGE WORD COUNT FOR THE MONTH

Total Word Count:_____ Divided by _____ days =_____

TOTAL FOR THE YEAR

Word Count:_____   Marketing Hours:_____
Brainstorming Hours:_____   Research Hours:_____
Editing Hours:_____   Reading Hours:_____

JOURNAL

What was your **top week**?

_____

What made your **top week** successful?

_____

What was your biggest **obstacle**?

_____

How did you **overcome** this? Or could do better next time?

_____

_____

What was your biggest **achievement**?

_____

_____

What **inspired** you most this month?

_____

Did you **discover** a new writing tip or advice this month?

_____

_____

TOTAL FOR THE MONTH

Word Count:_____   Marketing Hours:_____
Brainstorming Hours:_____   Research Hours:_____
Editing Hours:_____   Reading Hours:_____

TOTAL FOR THE YEAR SO FAR

Word Count:_____   Marketing Hours:_____
Brainstorming Hours:_____   Research Hours:_____
Editing Hours:_____   Reading Hours:_____

2021 is
Officially OVER!

Great job
staying accountable!

Time for your
Yearly Review!

YEARLY GRID BY ACTIVITY

Now, let's see what your activity looks like! This grid is designed to reveal what activities you do most in regards to the month or season even. You may be surprised that you do more writing at the start or end of the year. Take a moment and really pay attention to what you did, when you did it, and how you can best set your goals for the next year!

	WRITING OR WORD COUNT
	BRAINSTORMING
	EDITING
	MARKETING OR SOCIAL MEDIA
	RESEARCH
	READING
	OTHER:
	OTHER:
	OTHER:

YOUR AVERAGE WORD COUNT FOR THE YEAR

Total Word Count:_____ Divided by 365 =_____

What area did you spend the most time on?

_____

_____

What area should you work on n?

_____

_____

	J	F	M	A	M	J	J	A	S	O	N	D
1												
2												
3												
4												
5												
6												
7												
8												
9												
10												
11												
12												
13												
14												
15												
16												
17												
18												
19												
20												
21												
22												
23												
24												
25												
26												
27												
28												
29		■										
30		■										
31		■		■		■			■		■	

YEARLY GRID BY PROJECT

Let's take a look at your projects. If you were wondering why we were asking about this, we want to not only wanted to hold you accountable, but reveal some insight on how long it takes to complete them and how much of your year was spent on each one. Self-evaluation is important for prepping your goals for the year to come and also reveals about how much you really can do in the time you have. You might surprise yourself with the end result here!

What project did you spend the most time on?

Was this a bigger project or more difficult to complete?

	J	F	M	A	M	J	J	A	S	O	N	D
1												
2												
3												
4												
5												
6												
7												
8												
9												
10												
11												
12												
13												
14												
15												
16												
17												
18												
19												
20												
21												
22												
23												
24												
25												
26												
27												
28												
29		■										
30		■										
31		■		■		■			■		■	

THE YEAR IN REVIEW

THE RECKONING

How did you do? Did you do better or worse than expected?

_____

What prize or punishment did you award yourself?

_____

CAPTURE THE NOW

How do you feel right now?

_____

What are you wearing right now, Jake from State Farm? Where are you? Record this moment for Future You to enjoy.

_____

REFLECTION TIME

What habits or practices worked for you this year? Why do you think those worked for you?

_____

What obstacles did you struggle to overcome? How can you address those in the future?

_____

What lessons did you learn this year?

_____

FINAL THOUGHTS

Advice for your Former Self: What would you say now to Old You?

_____

Advice for your Future Self: What would you say to Future You?

_____

TOP TEN

> *"And remember, this is for posterity, so...be honest."*
> *--Count Rugen (The Princess Bride)*

1. Best song:_____

2. Best TV show:_____

3. Best movie:_____

4. Best book:_____

5. Best writing moment:_____

6. Best dialogue line:_____

7. Best tips/advice:_____

8. Best life moment:_____

9. Best writing spot:_____

10. Best drink/food:_____

So I Failed...Now What?

You keep writing, that's what you do. Get back on the path and keep going. But it's probably a good time to reevaluate your goals. What is a more reasonable goal for you? Think about the reasons that caused you to fail this time. What can you do differently next time? What are some unanticipated issues you ran into this time? Why didn't you think they would be obstacles? What can you do to prevent more obstacles from knocking you off the writing path?

So I'm finished...Now What?

Yay!!! Cheer one more time for the level of amazingness that is you! Enjoy that sweet reward. You earned this. Relish the moment. Remember this feeling. (Maybe even write down how you feel right now, so you can remind Future You of what is possible.) Now, set the bar a little higher and push yourself to grow or attempt to hit the same goals twice in a row!

Keep that magic going. Keep doing what worked for you this time, and use it to write the next project. Create new rewards and punishments. Plan a new project. Get lost in another world that demands to be poured onto the page. Take note of what worked and what didn't. Like, literally write it down. Use those notes as a record of your writing journey. People change, and so does writing. Allow yourself to see the path you've been on (while looking forward to what comes next).

NEXT YEAR PREP

What projects do you want to complete next year?

_____

_____

_____

_____

_____

Make your Reading List for next year.

_____

_____

_____

_____

_____

Stay accountable

and grab the 2022 edition!

CPSIA information can be obtained
at www.ICGtesting.com
Printed in the USA
BVHW020034271221
624869BV00022B/805